BIOLOGICAL ANTHROPOLOGY
A HOLISTIC APPROACH TO STUDYING MANKIND

Edited by Lakhbir Singh
Chabot College

cognella™
San Diego, CA

To
My Family
For Spreading the Fragrance of Anthropology
E v e r y w h e r e

Although I am responsible, without a doubt, for the book's viewpoints and how they unfold, this does not mean that all of these ideas and concepts are originally mine, either entirely or even partially. In my journey through anthropology, I stand on the shoulders of giants.

CONTENTS

Before Darwin, Most People Believed That All Species Had Been Created Separately and Were Unchanging

JAY PHELAN

C harles Darwin grew up in an orderly world. When it came to humans and our place in the world, in the mid-19th century the beliefs of nearly everyone were virtually unchanged from the beliefs of people who had lived more than 2,000 years earlier. Biblical explanations were sufficient for most natural phenomena: the earth was thought to be about 6,000 years old. With the occasional exception of a flood or earthquake or volcanic eruption, the earth was believed to be mostly unchanging. People recognized that organisms existed in groups called species. (In Chapter 10 we discuss in more detail what a species is; for now, we'll just say that individual organisms in a given species can interbreed with each other but not with members of another species.) People also believed that all species, including humans, had been created at the same time and that, once created, they never changed and never died out. This was pretty much what Aristotle had believed more than two millennia earlier.

Before he left this world, Darwin had thrown into question long and dearly held beliefs about the natural world and forever changed our perspective on the origins of humans and our relationship to all other species. He didn't smash the worldview to pieces all at once, though, and he didn't do it by himself.

In the 1700s and 1800s, scientific thought was advancing at a rapid pace. In 1778, the respected French naturalist Georges Buffon began to shake things up by suggesting that the earth must be about 75,000 years old. He arrived at this age by estimating that 75,000 years was the minimum time required for the planet to cool from a molten state. In the 1790s, Georges Cuvier began to explore the bottoms of coal and slate mines and found fossil remains that had no obvious similarity to any living species. The implications of Cuvier's discoveries were unthinkable, since biblical accounts did not allow for species to be wiped out. Cuvier's publications documented giant fossils (including the Irish elk, the mastodon, and the giant ground sloth) that bore no resemblance to any currently living animals. These fossils allowed only one explanation: extinction was a fact. Troubling as this observation was for the prevailing worldview, it was only the beginning.

Not only was it starting to seem that species could disappear from the face of the earth, but the biologist Jean-Baptiste Lamarck suggested in the early 1800s that living species might change over time. Although his ideas about the mechanisms by which this change might occur were wrong—he thought that change came about through the use or disuse of features—his willingness to question previously sacred "truths" contributed to an atmosphere of unfettered scientific thought in which it was possible to challenge convention.

Perhaps the heretical ideas that most inspired Darwin were those of the geologist Charles Lyell. In his 1830 book, *Principles of Geology*, Lyell argued that geological forces had shaped the earth and were continuing to do so, producing mountains and valleys, cliffs and canyons, through gradual but relentless change. This idea that the physical features of the earth were constantly changing would most closely parallel Darwin's idea that the living species of the earth, too, were gradually—but constantly—changing.

Darwin and After

IAN TATTERSALL

As we've seen, Charles Darwin's *On the Origin of Species* did not burst forth into a world that was totally unprepared for the concept of evolutionary change—a world unwilling to accept it, perhaps, but hardly a world that was unfamiliar with most of the evidence that Darwin used to support his ideas. Certainly by 1859, the year of the great book's publication, there was more than enough evidence around to convince any open-minded observer of the reality of evolution. Darwin had been harboring his radical thoughts for nigh on thirty years, and indeed, the naturalist Alfred Russel Wallace had already come to a conclusion strikingly similar to his own in a succinct and altogether brilliant manuscript he sent back to England in 1858 from the remote Indonesian island of Ternate. Together with extracts from Darwin's writings, Wallace's manuscript, written in haste after the ideas it expressed had crystallized for its author during a bout of malarial fever, was promptly read at the Linnean Society, and it goaded Darwin into writing his book.

Remarkable though it may seem in retrospect, however, at the time few might have disagreed with the Society's president, who remarked, in his annual summing up of events, that "[t]he year has not been marked by any of those striking discoveries which … revolutionise … the department of science on which they bear." The idea of evolution was in the air in 1859, but it was not yet an idea whose time had irresistibly come. What in the end rapidly won the day for *On the Origin of Species* was not merely that Darwin was a respected naturalist to whom his peers would listen, but that in his book he documented his ideas in such eloquent, exquisite, and exhaustive detail. He produced a work of astonishing originality that, quite simply, could not be ignored, and he proposed a compelling mechanism to underpin his notions of change. It is certainly true that from the vantage point of the early twenty-first century we may tend to overestimate the influence of Darwin's ideas of natural selection on late nineteenth- and early twentieth-century evolutionary thought, but there is no doubt that, despite the resistance he initially encountered, it was Darwin who made the concept of evolution itself respectable and who set the framework for our modern understanding of how life on earth came to be the way it is.

Darwin has been the subject of numerous careers in the history of science and wrote so voluminously that by judicious quotation one can defend almost any evolutionary viewpoint as somehow "Darwinian." Nonetheless, the essentials of Darwin's theory of evolution can be quite simply expressed. His own capsule definition of evolution was "descent with modification": ancestral species give rise to descendants which do not exactly resemble them. In searching for a mechanism to explain how this might occur, Darwin faced a politico-religious problem as well as a scientific one: he had not only to come up with a plausible means of change, but also to first destroy the pervasive notion of the fixity of species. Darwin's solution was simple. His studies of barnacles had already suggested to him that species were difficult or even impossible to recognize in the living fauna, with blurred boundaries between close relatives, but he delivered the *coup de grace* to their fixity by denying them identity in time. Here's how.

NATURAL SELECTION

In every generation, as animal breeders had long been aware, individuals of the same species vary in numerous ways. Those differences assure that some of those individuals are better suited than others to survive in any given environment. At the same time, in any generation many more individuals are born than will ever survive to grow up and reproduce themselves. It is the better adapted who will succeed in this winnowing process, and since traits are inherited, they will pass their superior adaptations on to their offspring. Each generation will thus be slightly different from the last, with more individuals possessing favorable adaptations and fewer having less well-adapted anatomies. In this way, over long spans of time, lineages will gradually become modified as they adapt to changing environments (or as they perfect their adaptations to existing environments) by the process Darwin named "natural selection."

This mechanism of change is not, Darwin stressed, in the least purposive; it consists merely of a sort of winnowing action achieved through the vagaries of the environment. Less well-adapted individuals contribute fewer offspring (resembling themselves) to the next generation, either through early mortality or through reduced reproductive effectiveness; those more favorably endowed live and produce more offspring (again resembling themselves). Most simply stated, then, natural selection is differential reproductive success.

It is central to this idea that offspring inherit their particular traits, advantageous or disadvantageous, from their parents: a fact that was obvious to anyone who had ever noted familial resemblance among relatives. Interestingly however, Darwin had no idea how this occurred. Indeed, Darwin's theories of inheritance were totally wrong, though he has escaped the pillorying for this deficiency suffered by the unfortunate Lamarck. What is significant, though, is that Darwin was perfectly able to formulate his enduring ideas on evolution *in the absence of* a valid theory of inheritance. This is a theme that we will return to later.

Now, while in one respect Darwin's ideas on evolution by natural selection ran counter to prevailing views of the fixity of species, in another way they were highly congenial to the spirit of the times in which he lived. For the Victorian ethos was one of progress, of improvement. Leave aside that the working classes labored in conditions of appalling privation; to those with the leisure to think about such matters the ubiquity of progress was evident. The explosion of technological change and economic expansion unleashed by the Industrial Revolution reached into all areas of nineteenth-century experience to inculcate a brash and optimistic view of the inevitability of progressive change and improvement. And this change was, of course, of an incremental, gradual sort: revolution was not simply undesirable, it was unthinkable. In this sense, Darwin's ideas were very much in tune with his times: whether consciously or not, he adapted to biology a more generally held notion of the inevitability of progress.

Nonetheless, once the furor that greeted the publication of his book had died down, it was for his gradualistic views on natural selection that Darwin was most strenuously criticized. Indeed, they continue to this day to be the focus of highly critical attention. In contrast, Darwin's central thesis, still the linchpin of modern evolutionary theory, was quite rapidly accepted by his peers though it was immediately more shocking to the general public. This central thesis is that all forms of life are related by ancestry. Darwin perceived the same pattern in nature that Aristotle and others had noticed in classical times and that had been rediscovered in the seventeenth century by Linnaeus and the other early systematists as they established the science of classifying the living world. A sort of hierarchy of similarity exists in nature, such that some organisms show more mutual similarity than others. All backboned animals resemble each other more than they resemble any animals without backbones, but within this group all mammals are more similar to each other than any is, say, to a turtle or to a hagfish. And primates have more in common with each other than any primate has with a cow or an opossum. Darwin's most basic insight was to see that this self-evident hierarchy of resemblance among living things exists as a result of genealogical relationship. This is a magnificently simple explanation for the pattern of nature, and the only one that predicts the pattern we actually find. Descent with modification: to Darwin this meant that all species, living and extinct, were descended from a single ancient ancestor, in a branching pattern that may be represented as we represent human genealogies, in the form of a tree or a branching bush.

In *On the Origin of Species* Darwin, as befitted the most cautious and unconfrontational of men, was as circumspect as he could possibly have been about the implications of all this for the relationships by descent of humans—even though these implications were dazzlingly obvious. "Light will be thrown on the origin of man and his history" was all he would say at this point. But heat, as might have been expected, ruled the day as the obvious conclusion was drawn. The most celebrated of the acrimonious exchanges that took place in the months following the publication of *Origin* was, of course, the encounter between Bishop Wilberforce and Thomas Henry Huxley, "Darwin's bull-dog," at the meeting of the British Association for the Advancement of Science in June l860, where the issues of human relatedness to the great apes were brought out into the open. At the time, the evolutionary view was widely caricatured as claiming human descent from the great apes themselves. This of course made marvellous newspaper and magazine copy; but most emphatically, the idea of common descent implies nothing of the kind. The apes, too, have become modified over the millions of years, separating us from our common ancestor, which was neither a modern human nor a modern ape.

EARLY DISQUISITIONS ON NEANDERTHALS

Huxley eloquently took the bull by the horns in 1863, when he published a small book of essays entitled *Evidences as to Man's Place in Nature*. The thrust of this work was to demonstrate through comparative anatomy that the apes resembled humans much more than monkeys did. In one essay he described what was known of the history and the habits of the apes; in another he showed how embryology and anatomy demonstrate the affinities of humans to primates in general, and to apes in particular (Darwin's notion of common descent providing the only plausible mechanism for this); in the third he looked at fossils that might bear on human evolutionary history. These were limited to the adult Engis cranium, which he correctly identified as a "fair average human skull, which might have belonged to a philosopher, or might have contained the thoughtless brains of a savage," and the Feldhofer Neanderthal. He was impressed by the distinctiveness of the Neanderthal skullcap but concluded, largely because it had contained a modern-sized brain, that this specimen could not "be regarded as the remains of a human being intermediate between Men and Apes." Although "the most pithecoid of known human skulls," it formed "the extreme term of a series leading gradually from it to the highest and best developed of human crania." It is perhaps curious that while Huxley was by instinct a saltationist who had chided Darwin in a letter that "[y]ou have loaded yourself with an unnecessary difficulty in adopting *Natura non facit saltum*—Nature does not make leaps so unreservedly," in his essay on the Neanderthaler he capitulated in just this way to the gradualist mindset.

This stance strictly limited Huxley's interpretive options. For despite the advantage of an evolutionary perspective, from which he was at least able to ask: "In still older strata do the fossilised bones of an Ape more anthropoid, or a Man more pithecoid, than any yet known await the researches of some unborn palaeontologist?" Huxley was able to see in these specimens no more than evidence for great human antiquity. He therefore added nothing to what Schaaffhausen had already proposed—beyond, perhaps, establishing brain size as a vital criterion for humanity. Worse, in refusing to acknowledge the distinctness of the Neanderthaler, he established the basis for a unilinear view of human evolution whose leaden hand has suffocated paleoanthropology ever since.

It is hard to fault Huxley too greatly for his failure to recognize in the Neanderthaler a distinctive entity: a product, perhaps, of one of Nature's leaps. After all, the entire suite of distinctive material at his disposal consisted of one bizarre and highly incomplete specimen that was comparable to nothing else known to science. Nevertheless, a year after Huxley published his observations, the Anglo-Irish anatomist William King drew emphatic attention to the "remarkable absence" in the Neanderthal cranium "of those contours and proportions which prevail in the forehead of our species; and few can refuse to admit that the deficiency more closely approximates the Neanderthal fossil to the anthropoid apes than to *Homo sapiens.*" Indeed, King argued that the specimen was so apelike as to "lead one to doubt the propriety of *generically* placing it with Man," although "in the absence of the facial and basal bones" to advocate this view "would be clearly overstepping the limits of inductive reasoning." Nonetheless, in contemplating the Neanderthal skull, King found himself compelled to conclude that the "thoughts and desires that once dwelt within it never soared beyond those of the brute," and in a footnote, suppressing his desire to place it in a separate genus, he created for the specimen the new species *Homo neanderthalensis.* King's was the first formal recognition ever that another human species besides *Homo sapiens* had existed on the Earth. And while its author was certainly bold in unhesitatingly arriving at this conclusion with just one fossil at hand, unbeknownst to him another specimen had already been found which demonstrated that the Neanderthal specimen was no aberration.

A fossil skull found in a quarry at Gibraltar had been found at some time prior to 1848, when it was brought to the attention of the Gibraltar Scientific Society. Unappreciated for what it was, it lay gathering dust in a small local museum until it was spotted by a visiting anthropologist in 1863. This gentleman arranged for it to be sent to London for examination by George Busk, Schaaffhausen's translator. The specimen itself clearly belongs to the same hominid species represented by the probably male Neanderthal individual, though it is considerably more lightly built and may represent a female. The cranial vault is long and low, and the forehead slopes sharply back from the eyebrows, which are adorned with distinct ridges. The vault protrudes rearward, while the face is large and somewhat projecting, with a wide nasal aperture and backward sweeping cheekbones. The significance of the Gibraltar skull was not lost on Busk, who immediately reported this proof that the Neanderthaler did "not represent … a mere individual peculiarity." The specimen was evidence that the Neanderthaler may indeed have represented a "[r]ace extending from the Rhine to the Pillars of Hercules." "Even Professor Mayer," Busk wrote, "will hardly suppose that a ricketty Cossack engaged in the campaign of 1814 had crept into a sealed fissure in the Rock of Gibraltar."

Alas! Busk's shrewd commentary fell on deaf ears. Huxley had taken to task Carter Blake, the secretary of the Anthropological Society in London, for suggesting that the Neanderthal bones were simply those of some poor idiot or hermit who happened to die in the cave. Yet pathology and idiocy (for certain inherited conditions that result in mental deficiency also involve abnormal development of the skull) continued to be favored explanations for the unfamiliar morphology of the Neanderthaler. This was especially true in Germany where the specimen, almost inevitably, became the center of an increasingly bitter controversy. The distinguished and antievolutionary pathologist and anthropologist Rudolf Virchow decided in 1872 that the Neanderthal individual was an aged man who had suffered rickets in childhood, head injuries in middle age, and chronic arthritis in his later years. These factors accounted for his odd morphology; and what's more, Virchow said, the fact that he was able to survive with these disabilities showed that he could not be ancient, for in a presettled society he could not have survived.

It was perhaps inevitable that the Neanderthal specimen, as the only truly distinctive early human then known, should become embroiled in the disputes over evolution itself in the years immediately following the publication of *On the Origin of Species*. But the variety of opinions that it elicited also reflected something else: the nascent science of paleoanthropology was just beginning to feel its way forward. With no other comparable fossils and no existing body of interpretation to provide an analytical framework, it is hardly surprising that almost every possible explanation for the odd appearance of the Neanderthaler was explored in the years immediately following its description. Disease, idiocy, trauma, the outer limit of normal variation, membership in a species totally discon-nected from modern humans—how many more possibilities could there be outside the realm of theology?

Well, one. The one, indeed, that most naturally occurs to (most of) us today. The Neanderthaler could have belonged to a species ancestral to humans, or to a collateral relative. But this idea was totally foreign to the received assumptions of the time, most of which dated back to well before the advent of Darwinism. For years a major concern among anthropologists had been the origin of the human races. Some held that these had diverged from a single origin; others thought that they had been separately formed. While the strict Biblical account of Creation held sway, the idea of a single origin in the Garden of Eden was naturally favored, but as the literal reading of Genesis lost ground in the later nineteenth century, the idea of multiple origins garnered more support. The Dutch science historian Bert Theunissen has pointed out that as Darwinist ideas caught on, both of these perceived possibilities of human racial origins were easily incorporated within an evolutionary context: either humans had diversified from one ancestral species or each race was descended from an extinct nonhuman species. Emphasis was placed on the differences between human races, rather than upon their similarities; and typological notions—essentially of fixed form—ruled the day. This was in fact rather ironic, since even back in Buffon's time it had been permissible to speculate about the tranformation of one infraspecific form into another, while it was now only permissible to talk in terms of transformation between species. But the upshot was that anthropologists could with little difficulty fit the Neanderthaler into the spectrum of defined human types as an added category. This was especially so since European scientists were prone to rank various perceived varieties of the human species on a scale of perfection that unsurprisingly placed them at the top. And since it was not uncommonly believed that the races at the top and bottom of the ladder were more dissimilar from each other than those at the bottom were from the apes, the Neanderthal type fit even more comfortably at the foot of this ranking.

Another reason for neglecting the possibility that the Neanderthaler was a human ancestor or collateral relative was that, as in some circles today, in the 1860s the fossil record was not thought to be central, or even particularly relevant, to the problem of sorting out evolutionary relationships. The proof of evolution was sought and found in comparative anatomical and embryological similarities: to a greater or a lesser extent organisms share structural features and developmental sequences, and it is these that reflect and are explained by their common descent. The ebulliently Darwinian German school of morphology, in particular, was based entirely on the use of comparisons among living organisms to elucidate the order inherent in natural diversity; indeed, the dictum of the great German embryologist Ernst Haeckel, that "ontogeny recapitulates phylogeny," virtually made not only the fossil record but the comparative study of adult organisms irrelevant to the clarification of evolutionary relationships. And indeed, although Haeckel's belief that in its individual development each organism goes through all of the stages through which its antecedent species had passed is not literally true, it is nonetheless quite possible in principle to figure out relationships among extant animals without knowing anything of their fossil record. What fossils do, we now realize, is to both add a unique time dimension to our reconstructions of evolutionary history and enlarge the comparative base available to us. But in the mid-nineteenth century the human fossil record, while accepted as evidence of human ancientness, was simply not associated with the idea of human descent.

Theunissen has drawn attention to one other widely held belief that militated against accepting the Neanderthaler as a precursor of modern humans. From the early years of the nineteenth century onward, the belief gained ground that modern Europeans had not developed in situ, but were the descendants of people who had entered the region from somewhere in central Asia. Originally based on linguistic evidence of similarities between European languages and the more ancient Sanskrit of the Indian subcontinent, this idea gradually came to incorporate notions of race. By the third quarter of the nineteenth century, the so-called "Aryan hypothesis" had been elaborated to a point where it envisioned a late Paleolithic or Neolithic invasion of Europe by agricultural peoples from the south and east. These "superior" invaders supplanted the indigenous hunting peoples, who were assumed to have been wiped out or otherwise to have become extinct. The Paleolithic

Neanderthaler, then, could hardly have borne any direct relation to modern Europeans. Paleolithic Europeans were of incidental interest; human ancestry that mattered was to be sought in Asia. So while later finds, notably of two quite complete Neanderthal skeletons at the Belgian site of Spy in 1886, finally persuaded the world that here indeed was a distinct form of archaic human, few even then appreciated its significance. Indeed, quite amazingly, the precise relationship of the Neanderthals to ourselves remains debated to this day.

ANTIQUARIANISM TRANSFORMS INTO ARCHAEOLOGY

Even as the notion that, as Darwin put it, "species are the modified descendants of other species" was rapidly gaining favor among biologists, the antiquarians were transforming themselves into archaeologists and in the process establishing beyond doubt the ancientness of the human lineage. They were, moreover, moving beyond this more generalized goal to develop a chronology of the prehistoric human past. In 1865 the English archaeologist Sir John Lubbock published his *Prehistoric Times*, in which he adopted the scheme of successive Stone, Bronze, and Iron Ages already proposed by two Danish scholars, Christian Thomsen and Jens Jacob Worsaae. Lubbock further subdivided the Stone Age into earlier and later periods: the Palaeolithic, characterized by flaked or chipped stone tools, and the Neolithic, in which polished stone tools were used. It was already abundantly clear by 1865 that of all these periods the Paleolithic was by far the longest, and it was not long before it was in turn subdivided.

Progress toward this subdivision surged in the middle 1860s, when the paleontologist Edouard Lartet and a local aristocrat, the Marquis de Vibraye, began to explore the archaeological potential of the caves and rock shelters in the limestone landscape of the Dordogne region of western France. It had been known for years that shaped flints and bone were abundant in the earth [??] such sites in the Dordogne, though Lartet's attention had initially been attracted by sites further to the south, such as the rock shelter at Aurignac, southwest of Toulouse, which in 1852 had yielded a large number of human burials in association with an extinct fauna and stone tools.

In 1868 Lartet and the English banker Henry Christy excavated a small rock shelter in Les Eyzies de Tayac, a village in the valley of the Vezere River which was destined rapidly to become the "Capital of Prehistory." At this site, Cro-Magnon (as the rock overhang beneath which a Monsieur Magnon kept his farm implements was known in the local patois), workmen digging fill in constructing a road from the newly built railway station into the village had uncovered some human skeletons. Lartet and Christy's investigations revealed that at least five burials, one of an infant, had been made in the rock shelter. These people were of modern form but were associated nonetheless with stone tools and the remains of extinct animals. It was the Cro-Magnon site that gave its name to the first modern people of the Dordogne region and by extension of Europe as a whole.

Between 1865 and 1875 the various parts of Lartet and Christy's great Work *Reliquiae Aquitanicae* were published. In this landmark study Lartet and Christy suggested that although Le Moustier, Laugerie Haute, and La Madeleine, three of their sites near Les Eyzies, were clearly of the "age of simply worked stone without the accompaniment of domestic animals," they did not "possess a uniformity in the production of human industry." Clearly the Paleolithic had to be subdivided. As a paleontologist Lartet understandably tried to do this by means of the animals associated with the tools, recognizing a Cave Bear period, a Woolly Mammoth period, a Reindeer period, and so forth. Archaeologists, however, were unhappy with the idea of categorizing periods of human cultural development on the basis of zoological criteria, and it was not long before the archaeologist Gabriel de Mortillet reworked Lartet's chronology to correspond to the stone tool types that characterized the various periods.

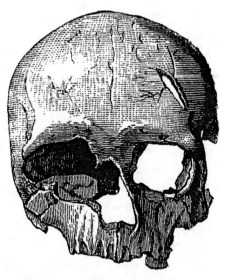

Skull of a Cro-Magnon woman. From *Die ersten Menschen und die prähistorischen Zeiten mit besonderer Berücksichtigung der Ureinwohner Amerikas*, Stuttgart 1884

De Mortillet's classification of 1872, enshrined in his great *Le Prehistorique* of 1883, recognized four periods of distinctive stone tool making in the Paleolithic. Each of these was named after the locality in which it was first or best represented. The oldest of these industries, or cultures, was the Chellean (later changed to Abbevillian), named for one of Boucher de Perthe's sites in the Somme Valley. Flint tools of this age included massive handaxes made by knocking flakes off a "core" until a standard shape was obtained. This was followed by the Mousterian, in which tools were fashioned on large flakes that had been detached from a core shaped to predetermine their form. Next came the Solutrean, characterized by incredibly finely worked "laurel-leaf" points. The final period, of the Paleolithic was the Magdalenian, when fewer tools were fashioned from stone and more were made of organic materials such as bone and antler. Later editions of de Mortillet's work added the Aurignacian period between the Mousterian and Solutrean (as the first period of the Upper Paleolithic) and inserted the Acheulean following the Chellean. In its essentials, this chronology of the Paleolithic survives today. Despite the general antipathy to Darwin's ideas that reigned in a France still in thrall to the shade of Cuvier, de Mortillet was also an enthusiastic Darwinian and was an early supporter of the idea that the roots of *Homo* were ancient indeed. He it was who coined the term "eoliths" (dawn stones), for the simple tools that he expected "Homo-simius," the human precursor, to have made.

As the complexities of the archaeological record of the Paleolithic were emerging, the earliest evidence of artistic activity by Aurignacian and later peoples was coming to light. As early as 1833 a baton and harpoon made of antler, both decorated with engraving, were found in the cave of Veyrier in Switzerland; and at around the same time an engraving of two deer on a plaque of reindeer bone was recovered from the French cave of Chaffaud. Thought by its discoverers to be Celtic, the Chaffaud piece was recognized by Lartet to be of Paleolithic origin, and he published it as such in 1861, along with an engraving of a bear's head which had been excavated in the cave of Massat in the foothills of the French Pyrenees. At Aurignac, too, engravings on bone had been found; and in 1864 Lartet and Christy published a detailed discussion of this evidence of ancient artistic activity. Objectively, there could be little doubt about the ancientness of such pieces. After all, most of them had been found in situ, buried under thick piles of sediment and in association with extinct animals whose representations they sometimes bore. And although the idea of prehistoric art took some time to be absorbed by the establishment, by 1867 the veracity of Paleolithic "portable" art was sufficiently well established that fifty-odd examples of it were placed on exhibit in the great Universal Exposition, held in Paris that year.

Cave art from the Paleolithic took much longer to be accepted, however. The first discovery of decoration inside a cave was that of the spectacular painted ceiling of the cave of Altamira, in northern Spain, by the young daughter of Don Marcelino Sanz de Sautuola. As her father was excavating in the floor of the cave in 1879, searching for prehistoric artifacts, she (who alone could stand upright beneath the low ceiling) looked up and saw in the lantern light the now-famous polychrome representations of bison, horses, and other large mammals. Her father recognized the similarities between these images and the engravings with which he was already familiar from portable art and quickly concluded that the paintings were indeed Paleolithic. Initial reaction to de Sautuola's amazingly insightful publication of this remarkable find was favorable, but in academic circles a reaction soon set in, and Altamira was condemned as a fake by one prehistorian after another. Supporters of de Sautuola were soon in a tiny minority, and it was not until near the end of the century, when corroborating finds began to be made at other sites, that opinion turned in de Sautuola's posthumous favor, and the cave art of the Upper Paleolithic was finally accepted as genuine.

Human Welfare Program

PROFESSOR DR. I.J.S. BANSAL

A human welfare program as such is a multifactorial concept and discipline that various scientific and even nonscientific approaches work to achieve. Even anthropology encompasses in itself different subdisciplines of human welfare. Each expert in these branches of anthropology has an equally important role to play in the welfare of a human society. Biological anthropologists, social anthropologists, environmental anthropologists, demographists, and so on, have equal and important contributions to make any welfare program a success. At the same time, it is not possible for any single individual who specializes in a particular branch of anthropology to speak for all areas of the subject. As a physical anthropologist trained in human genetics, I will make some observations about how a geneticist and genetics programs can contribute toward human welfare programs.

It is often said that a sound health and sound mind create a healthy society. Health care constitutes one of the important chapters in a human welfare program.

The health of a community is measured in terms of disease reduction. A natural history of disease clearly demonstrates that disease is caused by multiple factors that may be related directly or indirectly to humankind and their environment. In any case, disease can be biological, nutritional, chemical, physical, or genetic. In this regard the question of possible association between the genetically determined markers in the blood and specific diseases has received significant attention by physical anthropologists working in the field of human genetics. Several comprehensive genetic studies of various diseases and disorders that have already been undertaken by P.A. and ABO blood group polymorphism provide for the most extensively studied erythrocyte marker.

A possible association between blood groups and diseases, when established, will provide important clues toward understanding the specific biological function and its use as a diagnostic tool to delineate the degree of susceptibility of the individual to invasion by various parasites. Cases of such established associations have helped toward interpret the characteristic and geographical distributions of some of the numerous genetic polymorphisms (it has been realized by workers that cross-reading substances similar to blood group antigens are present on the cell walls of a number of pathogenic organisms (e.g., e. coli) and might in fact determine susceptibility of the individual to invasion by such pathogenic organism).

As already mentioned, sound health should be disease free, especially genetically so. So genetics itself is a major component of health and a healthy society. As such, the basic gradients of a healthy society are genes or a concept of genetics, and in our case human genetics. But for anthropologists the meaningful approach to these components should be in reference to the welfare of society. Human genetics is to my mind a very important factor with the present theme. So I begin with genetics and see how it is related to the best health program. Humankind's body, his mind, his physical and mental well-being are all products of the interaction between his inheritance and the environment that he encounters in the course of his life. The human body, like that of any living organism, owes its structure to the interaction of many genes. A change in any of these may affect the normal functioning of the organism and such changes can be inherited. The science of genetics, including human genetics, has been making rapid progress and in last few years has witnessed the gradual transition from Mendelism to the modern concept of molecular genetics. The structure and function of the gene involves not only the individual carrying it but also the family in which it segregates and the population in which it exists. The interplay of forces, which determines the incidence of inherited traits in a population, needs investigations by population geneticists. The human gene pool is profoundly affected by changes in the environmental conditions as well as changes in mating behavior of different populations. This results in changing the frequencies of different genetic constitutions that are primarily responsible for the biological basis of the health of a population.

Genetic markers and their association with diseases have played an important role in effective health care of individuals and the group. These diseases, which affect health (one factor could be food, etc.), could be purely genetic in origin, environmental in origin, or the result of complex interaction between the two. Understanding diseases and their correlates has often come through the pioneering efforts of physical anthropologists trained in human genetics.

But with the comprehensive knowledge of genetics, the existing health program and the infrastructure are being geared to provide comprehensive health care, especially to the mother, the maternal and infant mortality. Many investigations have also been made to measure the impact of gene frequency distribution on the existence of fertility, infertility, and mortality pattern in the background of prevalent sociobiological conditions that have a great bearing on health status.

So it can be seen that the study of human genetics plays a very important role in the welfare of mankind to provide disease free health. Certainly knowledge in genetics affect the attitude towards life, death, and health. The advances in human genetics during the past twenty years have revolutionized knowledge of the role of inheritance in health and disease. We know that our DNA determines not only the cause of catastrophic single gene disorder, which affect the millions of persons worldwide, but also our predisposition to cancer, heart disease, and many other disorders and to some infectious diseases. When used properly, this knowledge will be extremely important and acceptable only if their application is carried out ethically, with regard to autonomy, justice, education, and the beliefs and laws of each region and community, especially tribals. The application of genetic knowledge must be carried out for doing good to individuals and families, not doing harm, offering right of choice after information is given and facilitating personal and social justice. We inherit our genes from our parents, pass them to our children, and share them with our close involves many people. It is then ethically imperative that genetic studies should be used only to the advantage of the members of a family or ethnic group and never to stigmatize or discriminate against them. Application of genetic knowledge should not be compulsory for individuals or population. They should be free to refuse or accept as per their wishes and moral belief. In this regard they should be preinformed and educated about the purpose and possible outcome of the results. Genetic services for prevention, diagnosis, and treatment of disease should be available to all. Data relevant to health care should be provided to the advantage of the individual and community. Education about genetics for the public and health care professional should be considered of paramount importance. Many people may abuse of genetic knowledge also. It is therefore important that genetic principles relevant to human health be emphasized appropriately for all people in all cultures.

It is also well known that quality of life is dependent on interaction between genetic endowment and environmental conditions, and later influenced by nutritional, socio-economic, cultural, and other factors. Most of the diseases, as I understand, have some genetic influence in their expression. A number of genetic disorders are being recognized from time to time—some are rare but many of these occur frequently. Susceptibility and resistance to various diseases at an individual level, a family level, and a group level also have a genetic basis.

Death and disease have often confounded humankind. Attempts to understand the disease and alleviate the suffering of human beings gave a tremendous impetus to medical research. As a result of the availability of advanced therapy it has been possible to conquer many diseases to a large extent. The development of technological tools for identifying the cause of diseases is also a great contribution to health care.

Understanding of the natural history of disease and its correlates has often come through the pioneering efforts of human biologists who followed the comparative approach in the study of the phenomenon of illness. Collaborative efforts of other medical specialties have brought forth comprehensive knowledge about disease. The complexity of disease manifestations in relation to the environmental correlates and the variability in such manifestations are still not well understood. It especially calls for extensive research on diseases that are prevalent in our country. The multifaceted holistic approach of human biologists/geneticists/medicos in collaboration with other specialists can provide the answer.

Looking into the future, I can also foresee that more and more disease of environmental origin, primarily parasitic or bacterial, will be controlled by preventive measures or through prophylactic treatment. I envisage that the diseases which are basically genetic and genetic-environmental in nature have been identified and will be identified in future by the human biologists.

As previously mentioned, the impact of genetics on the existing fertility, infertility, and mortality pattern in the background of prevalent sociobiological conditions are also to be seen.

Such detailed information will invariably lead to the understanding of high risk groups and facilitate clinical assessments of the recommended types of medical care. But how best can this information be utilized for the welfare of human beings? It is through counseling that couples pre-maritally make physician aware of the importance of such investigations in assessing high-risk pregnancies. Western countries have followed a combined approach. Consequently, a better awareness among parents has generated a demand of such services for the assessment of the risk factors; as a result, large numbers of mishaps have been and are being averted. In India, since the majority of the deliveries take place at home, the situation was confusing earlier. However, it is improving now. In urban areas the deliveries are mostly taking place at health centers. To begin with, these centers can be equipped for undertaking such investigations. It will not be out of place to emphasize the inclusion of genetic specialties as one of the components of the integrated approach to the health care being developed, and it will also need the optimum utilization of the talent in this specialty available in the country.

Birth of a malformed child is often looked down upon. Every parent has the right to know about his future progeny, particularly in cases where there is an affected child. This is possible only when we have baseline data on which the empirical risk figures could be calculated. But in any case these are all in terms of relative risks. People educated about these genetic anomalies view the sociobiological and psychological background of the parents in a process named genetic counseling.

It has been seen that in many genetic and genetic-environmental disorders the simple management approaches like modification of diet or life style, replacement of gene products, eliminator of excessive accumulation, or suppression of abnormal metabolites and surgical ablation of certain organs can help in reducing the otherwise serious effects of the disease manifestation that often results in a permanent handicap or may even be fatal.

I have made some of the observations on diseases vis-à-vis health care. It is impossible for a single person to touch on all the problems and strategies for better health. I feel that specialists who have gathered here from all over the country will be in a better position to discuss various problems confronted with health care.

There are many problems relating to the health of the tribals, starting from genetic ones, malnutrition, and diseases relating to local environmental conditions. There is a great need to help these people have a good health status. It is much more needed among them than in urban societies. Urban people can take care of health hazards themselves in view of the many facilities available in the metro and other big cities to overcome these hazards; but for tribals, such facilities are to be created by Govt. Non Govt. and other voluntary organizations. But before introducing any health program among tribals, we must assess the existing health status of the people of that area.

I strongly feel that any program to be successful must be accepted by the people for whom the program is planned. This is only possible if we have the basic data of the parameters connected with the health status of the tribal group. Once it is achieved the health welfare program should be designed accordingly. Tribals should be convinced that such programs are meant for their welfare and betterment.

To achieve a better health status for tribals the role of primary health centers (PHC) is very important but their functioning has not been up to the desired results. To my mind these centers have to be made more effective. The working style and financial position of various government departments are the major factors for these PHCs not functioning up to our expectations. I am of the opinion that voluntary organizations can come to the rescue. There should be a setup of professional volunteers, including medicos, anthropologists, social workers, and so on, who could stay in the field by rotation, and donors should contribute to equipment, medicine, and other infrastructure for these PHCs. There can also be the possibility of attaching mobile PHC dispensaries of every sensitive area of the tribals.

In most cases people are not able to reach PHCs because they are located at a far distance, and in absence of any mode of transportation they cannot reach the facilities in these centers. Mobile dispensaries can serve the purpose of health care to a limited extent for these people. The number of PHCs should also be increased (1-1 Lakhs center 10,000 subcenter).

Professor U.R. Rao in his presidential address at the 83rd session of the Science Congress outlined three factors for overall development of the Society: food, economy, and health security. Although he talked of these factors in general for the society, I feel that his points are very much true for tribal society also whether we talk in terms of urban society or tribal society. The fact remains that this can be achieved only through development in scientific knowledge and some type of industrial growth, and I do not mean here the industry of either higher, middle or lower magnitude but of cottage industry that can very well be established in these areas as a large number of these areas have raw material available in abundance and skill of the tribal people can make this type of industry possible. It is just a matter of exploiting and tapping the sources. It is a hard fact that economic sufficiency also contributes a lot to the health status of the tribal people. The proper planning to achieve this is based on coordination of activities and thinking of anthropologist, medicos, philanthropists, social workers, persons connected with cottage industry at the government level, bank people who can give loans to start such industries, and tribal society at large. A proper interaction of these components is therefore highly desirable for healthy and balanced growth of the tribal society.

A question is often asked as to why health welfare schemes meant for tribals, even for nontribals to some extent, do not yield the desired results. One of the major factors that I see in this regard is the lack of coordination between planner and field workers. Look at the situation. A scheme is announced by politicians; administrative officers plan and execute the scheme without knowing the real grassroots social, biological, environmental, and other such factors of the area of the welfare scheme. And let me know in such schemes how many anthropologists, medicos, or other field workers are usually committed for planning and execution of the scheme. I am of the firm opinion that there has to be a coordinated effort of the people of various disciplines already mentioned to make a health program of the tribals and for that matter any community group a success. It cannot be worked out on the concept of a single approach. Techniques available for growth studies are good measures and indicators of health. I have intentionally not touched it, as I do not come from that area of specialization. But I can see many in the gathering here who will be doing justification to this aspect.

I have pondered on some of the points with respect to health and genetics to the welfare program as these came to my mind. I am sure there will be many more aspects on this theme that I have not touched but which will surely be deliberated meaningfully and fruitfully in these two days.

With these words I convey my best wishes for the seminar and feel immense pleasure in presenting my thoughts to the theme of the seminar.

Thanks a lot for patiently listening.

Walking Through Time

ROBERT BOYD AND JOAN B. SILK

W ho has not walked barefoot on a beach of crisp sand and, bemused, examined the trail of footprints, paused, then looked back, to see the tide wiping them away? So ephemeral are the traces of our passing.

Yet, astonishingly, the tracks of extinct animals have survived for aeons under nusual circumstances of preservation, recording a fleeting instance millions of years ago. Preservation of such traces occurs under conditions of deep burial whereby the sand or mud into which the prints were impressed is changed into stone, later to be exposed by erosion.

When, in 1978, fossil footprints of an extinct human ancestor were discovered during a palaeontological expedition led by Dr. Mary Leakey, scientific and public attention was immense. The prints, partly exposed through erosion, were discovered at the site of Laetoli, to the south of the famed Olduvai Gorge in Tanzania, where Louis and Mary Leakey did their pioneering work researching human evolution.

The footprints at Laetoli, dated at around 3.6 million years, resolved one of the major issues of contention in palaeoanthropology (the study of early mankind), a field characterized by fierce rivalries of discovery and interpretation. At Olduvai, Laetoli, and other sites in Africa and beyond, the search for evidence regarding human development has focused on the discovery of fossilized bones. But while fossils have been the primary means of understanding our past, they cannot yield all the answers to the great debates that have beset the study of human evolution. One debate has been over the development of the brain in relation to our ancestors' ability to walk upright. Since Darwin's time it was thought that once upright posture and bipedalism had developed, the hands were then free to evolve manipulative skills. Stone tool making, it was supposed, was the critical factor in the emergence of early man. This view, however, was not universally accepted. Some believed that "the brain led the way," not erect posture. Although functional analysis of hominid bones from Africa pointed to early bipedalism, the fossils themselves could not provide the definitive answer.

The Laetoli trackway settled the issue. Excavated by Mary Leakey and her team in 1978 and 1979, the trackway consists of some 70 footprints in two parallel trails about 30 meters long, preserved in hardened volcanic ash. The best-preserved footprints are unmistakably human in appearance, and yield evidence of soft tissue anatomy that fossil bones cannot provide. It is significant that the earliest stone tools known are about 2.6 million years old, made nearly a million years *after* the footprints at Laetoli. The Laetoli hominids were therefore fully bipedal well before the advent of tool making—an event considered to define the beginning of culture—and the traces they left behind provide evidence that the feet led the way in the evolution of the modern human brain.

THE CONSERVATION PROBLEM

The footprints at Laetoli, recorded by the Leakey team using various techniques including molding, casting, and photogrammetry, were reburied in 1979 as a means of preservation. After the trackway's reburial, the site revegetated. Although its condition was not known, nor was it visited frequently because of its remoteness, it was feared that the trackway might be deteriorating because of the impact of root growth, especially from acacia trees.

Following a request to the [Getty Conservation] Institute by the Tanzanian Antiquities Unit for assistance in conserving the site, a GCI-Tanzanian team undertook a preliminary investigation in mid-1992. The team opened a 3-by-3 meter trench which confirmed fears that root growth had caused damage, though the full extent could not be determined. Where root growth had not affected the tracks, preservation was excellent, validating the Leakey team's decision to rebury the site, and confirming a practice increasingly adopted by archaeologists to conserve excavated sites.

In 1993, field testing was undertaken by the project team, and a year later 69 trees on the burial mound were poisoned, the site mapped, and measures taken to prevent erosion. In addition, the original cast of the trackway, stored at Olduvai since 1979, was remolded to make a new master cast and additional casts were made with the assistance of staff from the National Museum of Tanzania. Since the trackway itself was too fragile to be remolded, the master cast provides the most accurate replica possible. The new casts also guided re-excavation of the trackway.

In the subsequent two years, campaigns were undertaken during the dry season. A joint team of specialists, including conservators, archaeologists, scientists, and photogramme-trists, re-excavated half of the trackway, recorded its condition stereophotographically, extracted stumps and roots, stabilized the surface, and reburied it using synthetic geotextile materials layered into the overburden of sand and soil. Geotextiles provide protection against root penetration, yet allow the trackway surface to "breathe"—that is, to maintain moisture equilibrium between the subsurface of the trackway and the atmosphere. For a period during the field work, the site was open to palaeoanthropologists for further study. Because of its fragility, it could only be exposed for a very limited period. Upon completion of the fieldwork a monitoring and maintenance plan for the site was designed for implementation by the Tanzanian authorities to ensure the long-term survival of the tracks. Meetings with the local community and a traditional blessing ceremony by the Masai religious leader and healer in the area—the *Loiboni*—were held to emphasize the significance of the trackway and explain the need for its protection.

Many opinions were voiced as to the best method to save the tracks, and the strategy of reburial was debated at length. Among other ideas have been proposals to uplift the entire trackway (or only the individual footprints) and move it to the National Museum in Dar es Salaam; or, to build a shelter over the site and open it to the public. The latter is impractical, at least for the moment, because of the site's remoteness and difficulty of access, and the lack of infrastructure for displaying, staffing, and securing the site. The former assumes that the tracks have scientific value only and thus overlooks their cultural significance.

The Laetoli footprints are the most ancient traces yet found of humanity's ancestors. To move the site *in toto* or, worse, to remove only the prints, would be contrary to the widely accepted ethic of conservation in context. The prints were impressed in volcanic ash in that location 3.6 million years ago, in sight of the Sadiman volcano 20 kilometers away, whose subsequent ash falls buried them under 30 meters of deposit. Over the aeons the landscape eroded; until less than a few inches of soil covered the surface at the time of discovery. Powerful arguments can be mustered to save the site in its original setting. The Tanzanian authorities themselves committed to this approach.

It is indisputable that burial is an effective preservation measure, if other requirements such as vegetation control through maintenance are also met. Only if these criteria are not achievable should other options be considered. While lifting the tracks is doubtless technically possible, it would be enormously costly, require much research, and risk damage or loss. For these reasons, the decision to rebury the site has been made, and if future conditions allow the site to be opened to visitors, it will have been saved.

Because the Laetoli tracks have been reburied, a permanent display was installed at the Olduvai Museum, which overlooks the gorge where Mary and her husband, Louis S. B. Leakey, made so many of their famous discoveries. The Laetoli room displays the cast of the trackway and photographs and text (in English and Swahili) that explain why the site was reburied and how it is being protected.

TRANSCENDING TIME

The footprints at Laetoli represent an immense distance in time. While we are used to bandying terms like "a million years," we cannot really comprehend them on a human scale. We are comfortable with one or two thousand years. They are within the frame of recorded history, spanning the last few hundred human generations. The Laetoli tracks are of another dimension, taking us back perhaps more than one hundred and eighty thousand generations.

The question has been asked why the Getty Conservation Institute, whose work is preservation of the cultural heritage, should be involved in saving a fossil site, even one of immense significance in the study of evolution. The answer to this question will be clear to those who have trod the beach and pondered their own trail of footprints, for there can be scarcely anything so evocative as the Laetoli trail marking humanity's long, wondrous, and mysterious journey. As a nexus between cultural heritage and science, so often un-comprehended in today's world of big science, the footprints are a poignant reminder of our ancient origins. Let Mary Leakey have the last word in talking of one of the hominids who made the trail: "At one point, and you need not be an expert tracker to discern this, she stops, pauses, turns to the left to glance at some possible threat or irregularity, and then continues to the north. This motion, so intensely human, transcends time. Three million six hundred thousand years ago, a remote ancestor—just as you or I—experienced a moment of doubt."

The Evolution of Menstruation

ROBERT BOYD AND JOAN B. SILK

enarche and menopause mark the beginning and end points of women's reproductive careers. During the years between menarche and menopause, women undergo cyclic changes in their ability to conceive and sustain a pregnancy. In humans, these monthly cycles are marked by conspicuous vaginal bleeding, or menstruation, and are therefore known as menstrual cycles. For many women, menstruation is an innocuous reminder of their reproductive status. For others, menstruation is more problematic. Menstruation is sometimes associated with unpleasant symptoms, ranging from bloating to severe cramps and anemia. Some women complain of irritability, moodiness, fatigue, headaches, and other problems just before menstruation begins, a collection of symptoms that has become known as **pre-menstrual syndrome,** or **PMS.** Recently, behavioral ecologists have begun to consider why these cycles occur and why women menstruate. To understand their hypotheses, we need to know something about the events that characterize the menstrual cycle.

All mammalian females experience cyclic changes in their ability to conceive and to become pregnant. These cycles are generally known as ovarian cycles, rather than menstrual cycles, because external bleeding is the exception rather than the rule among mammals. The central event in each ovarian cycle is ovulation, the development and release of a mature egg cell from the ovaries. Although the full complement of egg cells is present at birth, the development of egg cells in the ovaries is halted at an intermediate stage. During each ovarian cycle, a single egg cell is somehow selected for development. But before the lucky egg is ready to be released from the ovary, certain preparations must be completed: the egg cell must resume its arrested activity, and the uterus must be prepared to sustain a pregnancy. Hormones secreted by the pituitary gland and the ovaries regulate these processes.

The pituitary hormones, **follicle-stimulating hormone (FSH)** and **luteinizing hormone (LH),** stimulate the development of the ovarian steroid **estradiol** (a form of estrogen) by the follicle, a packet of cells that surrounds and nurtures each egg cell. As levels of estradiol rise, the follicle increases greatly in size and complexity. Just before ovulation occurs, levels of FSH, LH, and estradiol peak.

Estradiol and another ovarian steroid, **progesterone**, play an important role in preparing the uterus to sustain a fetus in the event of successful conception. Rising levels of estradiol stimulate the growth and development of the uterine lining, or endometrium, and the thickening of the **myometrium**, the layer of smooth muscle that lies underneath the endometrium. Estrogen also stimulates the endometrium to produce receptors for progesterone. Progesterone, in turn, promotes the development of glands in the endometrium that secrete glycogen and vital enzymes into the uterus. At the same time, the arteries that supply the endometrium join together, forming pools of blood in the endometrial tissue. If pregnancy does not occur, the tissue, secretions, and blood that have been accumulated in anticipation of pregnancy are shed. In most animals, these materials are reabsorbed into the body. In a few species, including humans, they are discharged from the body through the vagina. This is the phenomenon that we know as menstruation.

At first, it may seem inefficient to prepare the uterus repeatedly for pregnancy and then to abandon these preparations if pregnancy does not occur. After all, it is cheaper to leave a house standing that is intermittently occupied than to destroy and rebuild it every month. However, University of Michigan anthropologist Beverly Strassman argues that this is a poor metaphor because metabolic tissue is not made of inert substances, like brick or wood. Living tissue must be nourished, and this nourishment requires energy. Strassman suggests that it would actually be more energetically expensive to maintain the uterus in a state of continual readiness for pregnancy than it is to cycle regularly. Metabolic rates are 7% lower during the follicular phase, which precedes ovulation, than during the luteal phase, which follows ovulation. Women consume 11% to 35% more calories per day during the luteal phase than during the follicular phase. Similar patterns are seen in other mammalian species. Thus, if the uterus was always maintained in the luteal phase condition, females would need to increase their food intake substantially. Strassman estimates that women save six days' worth of food over four menstrual cycles. During the 12 months of lactational amenorrhea, women save nearly half a month's food. Since females' ability to reproduce successfully is typically limited by the availability of food, cyclical changes in readiness for pregnancy offer females a way to reduce their energetic requirements.

Although Strassman's argument provides a plausible explanation for ovarian cycling, it does not necessarily explain why women menstruate. After all, all mammalian females experience ovarian cycles, but conspicuous menstrual bleeding is relatively uncommon. Among primates, overt menstrual bleeding occurs only in Old World monkeys and apes.

Two hypotheses have been proposed to explain why menstruation occurs. Marjorie Profet has suggested that menstruation evolved to rid the uterus of pathogens carried by sperm. Strassman has criticized Profet's hypothesis and contends instead that menstrual bleeding is simply a side effect of ovarian cyclicity and has no adaptive function.

Profet's hypothesis is that menstruation evolved to protect the uterus and other reproductive organs from being colonized by pathogens carried by sperm. Strassman has examined several predictions derived from this hypothesis. First, if menstruation defends the uterus against pathogens, then uterine infections should be more common before menstruation than after menstruation. In fact, much the opposite is true. Menstruation seems to increase the risk of infection, perhaps because blood is an excellent medium for bacteria. Second, Profet argues that menstruation tracks women's exposure to sperm-borne pathogens, occurring during the portion of women's lives when they are sexually active. However, in traditional societies women do not menstruate for long periods when they are pregnant and lactating, even though they are sexually active during these periods. And women continue to engage in sexual activity after they have reached menopause. Thus, menstruation provides little protection to women during much of their sexually active lives. Third, Profet predicts that menstruation will be most copious among primate species in which females have multiple mating partners. However, comparative analyses across primates provide no support for this prediction. Thus, there is little evidence to support Profet's hypothesis that menstruation reduces the risk of infection by sperm.

Strassman contends that menstruation is not maintained by natural selection, but is instead a by-product of ovarian cycling. She suggests that variation in the degree of menstrual bleeding among primates may be related to anatomical differences in 1) the structure of blood vessels that supply the endometrial tissue with nutrients, 2) the thickness of the endometrium, or 3) the volume of the uterus. She points out that in Old World monkeys and apes conspicuous menstrual bleeding tends to occur in species in which females produce relatively large infants. In such species, there may simply be too much blood to reabsorb.

Heredity: Living Code in a Coil

SARAH R. RIEDMAN

A s man grew to know more and more about himself, he wondered more and more about heredity, both his own and that of the animals he had domesticated. And what about the differences between one human being and another? What makes one a mathematical genius and another a great musician, one an average person and another mentally retarded? How are certain characteristics passed on from parent to child? Why is a child born with a defect that seems to have cropped up in a particular family for the first time?

The science dealing with these questions is called "genetics," one of the most recently developed branches of biology.

Geneticists consider the *chromosomes* to be the basis of heredity. These are threadlike, deeply staining bodies present in the nucleus of every cell. There are twenty-three pairs of chromosomes in every human cell, and each chromosome is said to contain several hundred *genes* strung together in a row. The gene responsible for any particular trait, such as eye color, is said to have a particular position, or "locus," in the string.

Within the period of your lifetime, geneticists, biochemists and biophysicists, using the most advanced research tools, have greatly advanced our knowledge of chromosomes and the transmission of hereditary characteristics. The units of heredity may indeed be much smaller than genes, for the basic substance of heredity is now thought to be a single chemical, present in the nucleus of every cell of every living thing. This chemical's intricate structure is such that it possibly plays the central role in shaping the heredity of a particular human being. Also it is said to carry the hereditary information or blueprint for a wheat plant and a maple tree, a mouse and an elephant; to determine the color of your eyes and hair, your blood type, as well as everything that makes you a human. Yet, it itself may be

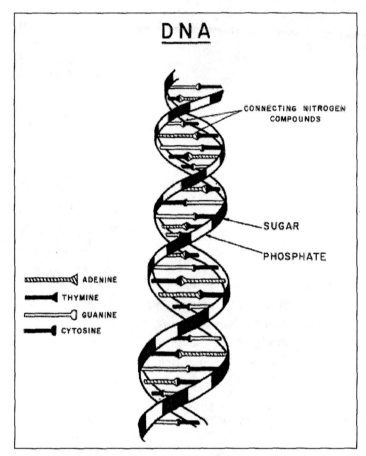

DNA

CONNECTING NITROGEN
COMPOUNDS

SUGAR

PHOSPHATE

ADENINE
THYMINE
GUANINE
CYTOSINE

The Crick and Waston scheme to show the structure of the DNA molecule.

changed either artificially or by chance in nature, thereby altering the heredity of an organism in a process called "mutation," which means "change."

This remarkable substance is known as DNA, short for d*eoxyribonucleic* a*cid*—its formal chemical name that stands for *deoxyribose* (a sugar) and *nucleic acid*. DNA is not a newly discovered chemical, but for nearly a century after it was extracted from the nuclei of pus cells, its function as a genetic material was not suspected. Then in 1944 a group of scientists working at Rockefeller Institute discovered that this particular nucleic acid—DNA—transformed the heredity of pneumonia-producing bacteria into harmless bacteria which continued to breed true; that is, their "descendants" also lost the power to produce disease. This astonishing finding, seemingly as unbelievable as a dog giving birth to kittens, was the beginning of a dramatic change in biologic thinking. And it spurred biologists and scientists in related fields to reorient their investigations into the mechanisms of heredity. In laboratories all over the world scientists carried out new and different experiments. It has been said that the decade between 1950 and 1960 was the most fruitful in the entire history of biology.

First, what is DNA? It is a gigantic, complex molecule, several million times as heavy as a hydrogen atom (the lightest of all elements). Yet DNA cannot be seen with the ordinary light microscope, for while the molecule is enormously long, it is also so thin that only the electron microscopes 100,000 times magnification reveals it as a long strand. DNA is made up of six chemical groups: *deoxyrihose, phosphate* and four groups called nitrogen bases. These six chemical groups, repeated several thousand times, are arranged in a double strand according to a specific pattern. Whether in an onion or a human sperm cell, DNA has the same general structure and chemistry, with only the arrangement and combinations of the four bases being distinctive for each living thing.

What is the structure of DNA? It is made up of two enormously long chains in which the sugar and phosphate groups are arranged alternately—a sugar and a phosphate, a sugar and a phosphate—and the two chains are cross-linked with pairs of the four bases. The bases are called *Adenine, Thymine, Guanine* and *Cytosine*. A and T always pair up, and so do G and C to form one cross-link. The A-T cross-links and the G-C cross-links are randomly arranged, but since A and G are long and T and C are short pieces, and the cross-links are all of equal length, A can never be linked to G, nor T to C. The two long chains with their cross-links are wound around each other in spiral fashion, so that the whole DNA strand resembles a spiral staircase with four steps or rungs between each turn. In geometric language, such a coil is called a *helix*. Unlike a corkscrew which is pointed at one end, a helix has the same width throughout its length, like a cylinder.

The DNA of different species of plants and animals differs in the length of the strand and in the amounts of the four bases. The DNA strands contained in a single human cell, if stretched out as one piece, have been estimated to reach a total length of about six feet with thousands upon thousands of cross-links. We may well ask how such a long structure can fit into the chromosomes, which are themselves microscopic in size. Well, exactly how the DNA is arranged is not known, except that the strands must be coiled and tightly packed

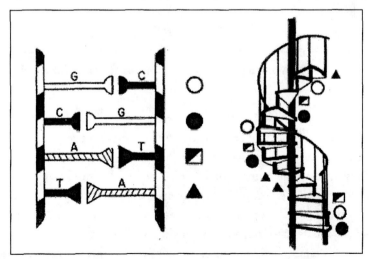

(LEFT) The arrangement of Adenine (A), Thymine (T), Guanine (G) and Cytosine (C), in one of the repeated sequences of four "steps" in DNA. (RIGHT). The "staircase" model of DNA.

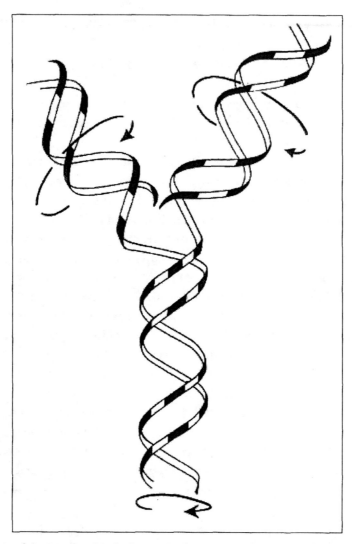

The unwinding of the DNA molecule during duplication and formation of two daughter cells.

in the chromosomes. But by weighing DNA molecules and breaking them up into their chemical groups, it is possible to determine how many of each of the bases there are in the DNA of a given species. And no matter what the species, one interesting fact is that the number of A's is equal to the number of T's, as is the number of G's to C's. However, the proportion of A-T pairs and G-C pairs varies widely in different species, and the ratio of one pair to the other identifies a particular species—rat or man, cabbage plant or oak tree.

How much of this is fact and how much theory? The actual chemical make-up has been unquestionably established. The differences in the amounts of the six chemical groups and their proportions in the DNA of different species has also been definitely determined. Much else that you will read about the role of DNA in heredity has also so far stood the test of an amazing volume of continuing experimentation. But let's take a glimpse at some of the milestones that lead to today's conception of the role of DNA in heredity.

In investigating this subject, biologists have borrowed the research tools of the chemist and biophysicist—tools that were necessary to verity what began with a hypothesis, a tentative idea, The biophysicist often works with what is called a "model"—a three-dimensional picture or architectural plan—that visualizes his idea of a particular molecular structure. Such a model for DNA was worked out in the Institute of Molecular Biology at Cambridge University, England.

As often happens in modern biological work, scientists with different types of training team up; in designing the model of DNA, the teammates were an English physicist and an American biologist. While their interests overlapped, the physicist had to fill in some gaps in his knowledge of biology, and the biologist had to learn to use the tools of the physicist. Before the work was completed a third team member was added—a New Zealand nuclear physicist who had participated in the project to separate uranium (at the University of California) during the development of the atom bomb.

These three men received the Nobel Prize in Medicine and physiology in 1962 for their work on the structure of the nucleic acids and the "significance for information transfer in living material." They were Francis H. C. Crick of Cambridge, England, James D. Watson of Harvard, and Maurice H. F. Wilkins who (at the time of this particular project) was working in a biophysics laboratory at Kings College, London.

Dr. Crick had contributed to the development of radar during World War II, and after the war turned to the flourishing new field of molecular biology, the study of life processes examined from the structure and operation of the molecules involved. Dr. Watson, now at Harvard University, received his doctorate in genetics at the University of Indiana and went to Europe for his postdoctoral study, where he joined Dr. Crick at the molecular biology unit at Cambridge. Dr. Wilkins had looked for a different subject than atomic physics, "casting around for a new field of research," and decided to apply his knowledge to the physics of life. He was the first to suggest that DNA might have a crystalline structure—a definite molecular shape, like a crystal of ice or sugar.

Here, one of the technics—X-ray diffraction crystallography—employed by the biophysicist provided the means for studying the "shadow" of DNA. Such a shadow is formed when X rays hitting at an atom or groups of atoms are scattered by the electrons in each atom. By shooting X rays through DNA fibers he got the idea that the molecule had the shape of a helix. This clue was then followed up by Crick and Watson in constructing their theoretical model with, of course, the six chemical groups in DNA.

Using thin wires for the long chains and thin metal plates for the four bases, and armed with the knowledge of chemical laws, the team decided that the long chains must be made up of alternating units—sugar and phosphate. Then they twisted the chains into the shape of a helix. But what about the bases? Attaching them to the outside of the helix, they found that they had to discard this arrangement because it did not fit the X-ray diffraction pattern. Then they tried hanging them to one chain at a time, inside the helix, and at right angles to the chain. But in what order? Two long pieces followed by two short pieces? This again would not fit into a helix, fit arranging the cross-pieces, it became clear that if a long piece (*adenine*) were hung on one chain, it would have to be matched up with a short piece (*thymine*) on the other chain. This turned out to be correct for the shape of a twisted ladder. It also fitted the chemical facts: in a molecule of DNA each base was found in equal amounts with its pair. Therefore, there had to be an equal number of A and T pieces, and also of G and C pieces.

They finally made a model of the six groups that was a spiral ladder with four steps of equal length in between each turn. The two pieces making up each rung of the ladder were joined together by a hydrogen bond that could easily be broken, as it would have to be if DNA was to split along its length during cell division. Also, both the total number of rungs (base pairs) and their order could vary without distorting the shape of the "staircase" model. In fact, as its designers soon realized, these had to vary if the model was to account for species differences of nearly two million different kinds of living things, as well as the differences in individuals of each of the species.

It was a sensible model, and its structure was confirmed by Wilkins' X-ray diffraction patterns of the DNA molecules. Also, when the DNA from different species was examined, the same pattern appeared every time, the only differences being in the number and proportions of bases, determined by the chemist.

LIVING CODE IN A COIL

The idea that a single substance with the over-all pattern of DNA could hold the key to the heredity of every living thing on earth staggered the imagination. First of all, that so many variations were possible from one basic substance seemed too simple to be true. But the creators of the model thought it was possible. For example, compare the number of possible variants of DNA with the number of words in the English language which can be made with the twenty-six-letter alphabet. When you take into account that a single strand of DNA may have thousands of base pairs arranged in different order, and that each chromosome may contain millions of strands, the number of different DNA "words" that can be "spelled out" is infinitely greater.

There was also the question of what happens when a cell divides and half the chromosomes go to each of the daughter cells. Does each cell get a copy of the DNA? How does DNA duplicate itself? Watson and Crick thought that the two chains probably began to unwind at one end, a few rungs at a time, the bases in each pair breaking at the weak hydrogen bond. Suppose that the first two bases are free strand were A and G. (Others of the four bases are freely floating in the nucleus.) If another A or G brushed up against these, they would not fit. Only a T and a C could attach themselves to form a new rung of either A-T or G-C. As the molecule continued to unwind and open, like a zipper, a few "rungs" at a time, the process repeated itself until each half of every rung found its mate, and the double strand of DNA duplicated exactly. It is, of course, possible that a chance mismatching will occasionally occur. Should that happen, a change in heredity either for better or worse could appear in that individual.

In the years following the announcement (1953) by Watson and Crick of the theoretical structure of DNA, the mass of experimental findings has pointed to the conclusion that in this molecule is contained a master plan or code for the heredity of each form of life. The geneticist calls DNA the "blueprint" for heredity. Furthermore, it contains "instructions" for every chemical reaction involved in the synthesis of proteins, the most important building blocks of living cells, Therefore, the development of tissues in growth, and the production of enzymes and hormones (all basically proteins) is directed by DNA.

Proteins are manufactured in the *cytoplasm—outside* the cell nucleus. How does DNA, contained in the nucleus, instruct the chemical machinery in the cytoplasm of the cell? The answer to this is to be found in another nucleic acid—RNA, abbreviated from *ribonucleic acid*. Like DNA, RNA can be identified chemically in all cells, but instead of deoxyribose, ribose is the sugar in RNA, and one of its four bases is uracil, instead of the cytosine in DNA. But how is RNA involved in the manufacture of the many thousands of different proteins produced by the cells?

All proteins are synthesized from smaller building blocks called *amino acids*, of which twenty are known. These amino acids are contained in *ribosomes*—minute bodies scattered through the cytoplasm, and revealed by the electron micro-electron microscope; scope; RNA also has been tracked down to the ribosomes. These tiny bodies are the chemical factories for manufacturing different proteins from an assortment of varying numbers of some or all of the amino acids. What determines the combination and sequence of the amino acids?

Experiments have shown that there are two kinds of RNA: a single long chain which acts as a template, or mold, called the "Messenger RNA"; the other, called "Transfer RNA," is made up of small fragments. Geneticists visualize the process of directed protein synthesis in this way: when the DNA helix begin to unwind, splitting into two, RNA fragments join the open part of the chain, duplicating that part of the DNA, as if making a copy of the blueprint. DNA impresses its pattern on the RNA fragment, which then moves out into the cytoplasm. This is the Messenger RNA carrying the DNA instructions to the RNA in the ribosomes. Circulating in the cytoplasm are free sections of Transfer RNA, each with a definite sequence of three bases, like a three-letter word made from three of the four bases which we will designate as A-B-C-D.

The three bases can be arranged in different orders such as ABC, BCD, CDD, AAA, BCA, DDA and so on. Each triplet is comparable to an RNA fragment which attached itself to one particular amino acid only. The RNA fragment delivers its matching amino acid to the long RNA chain in the ribosome. The amino acid hooks on at the appropriate spot, freeing the RNA fragment which then moves on to pick up another amino acid

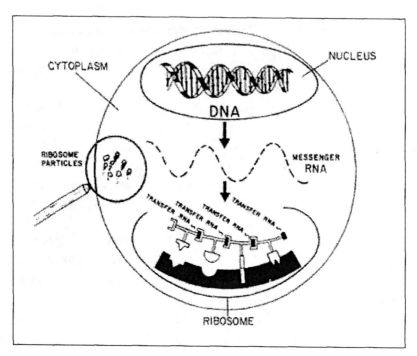

Summary scheme showing the role of DNA and RNA in the manufacture of proteins in the cell.

while the trailing amino acid joins with the one before. Eventually a long chain of amino acids is built up—link to link—into a complete protein. In this fashion the precise pattern contained in the DNA is passed on to Messenger RNA and Transfer RNA to construct the vast variety of body proteins.

That this process of assembling amino acids to produce proteins according to an RNA pattern by DNA really goes on in the ribosomes has been proved by following the steps with what the chemist calls "tracers": these are substances made radioactive artificially. The radioactivity acts like a label or tag which enables the chemist to detect the substance when it is taken up by a cell during synthesis or other process. The synthesis of protein by freely floating living cells has been followed by this method in test tube experiments. As the protein chain is formed in the presence of RNA, the amino acids—those originally added to the mixture containing living cells—disappear.

By this and other methods, the exact pattern or code of RNA fragments has been worked out for some amino acids. For example, the sequence UUU, a triplet of uracil, is the code for an amino acid called *phenylalanine*. Increasingly, the code is being broken for other amino acids. Finally, from such experiments the sequence of amino acids in one complete protein has been worked out. This protein is insulin, the hormone discovered by Banting. Insulin was found to consist of a total of fifty-one amino acids, containing sixteen of the twenty known amino acids.

It is not beyond possibility that the "profile" of much more complex proteins will eventually be drawn, and we may even look forward to the exact duplication of natural proteins in the laboratory. You can see how the coordinated efforts of chemists, physicists and biologists have paid off in monumental discoveries.

And so, while scientists are a long way from understanding what makes an Einstein, a Beethoven, a person with mechanical aptitude, one with "five thumbs," or for that matter one who is mentally deficient, the studies on DNA, RNA and protein synthesis begin to shed light on the very basis of life.

Death and the Sexes

JOHN F. KALINICH AND MAX FOGIEL

DNA DETERMINES YOUR SEX

The control gene that determines the sex of a human being is found on the Y chromosome. Of the 23 pairs of chromosomes, 22 pairs are homologous and 1 pair is not. These are the X and Y chromosomes, or the sex chromosomes. An individual with two X chromosomes is a female. An individual with one X and one Y chromosome is a male.

A person gets half of the genetic information from the father and half from the mother. The person must receive an X chromosome from the mother. The person can get either an X or a Y chromosome from the father. If a person receives an X chromosome from the father, then that person will be female. If a person receives a Y chromosome from the father, then that person will be a male.

Scientists studied what specific characteristics of the Y chromosome make a male. As technology improved, it became clear to scientists that just having the X or Y chromosome did not determine sex. There were individuals who had both an X and a Y chromosome and were female. There were also individuals who had two X chromosomes but were male. The DNA of the XX males revealed that these individuals carried a small part of the Y chromosome in their genomes. The small region contained the *sry* gene which is responsible for maleness. Scientists have used the mouse model to study sex determination.

The *sry* gene was added to the genes of a developing female mouse embryo. This experiment was used to test whether it was this gene that made an individual a male. This embryo grew to be a male mouse. This experiment proved that the *sry* gene could make an

XX female into a male. If nobody had this *sry* gene then everybody would be female. Sex determination is a marvelous mechanism. In a period of days, in a few thousand cells, one gene can influence the development of a male or a female. Individuals who have both an X and a Y chromosome, but are missing the *sry* gene, will develop as females.

Individuals can also have the X and Y chromosomes and the *sry* gene and be female. In this case, the cells were not able to understand the male switch. During development the *sry* gene was present and was switched on, and testes started to develop. However, the body could not recognize testosterone as a signal for maleness and testicular development was not completed. Not being able to understand the male testosterone signal is also a genetic condition.

Some disorders can be corrected if they are caught early in development. For example, there is a condition in which a baby can be born with two X chromosomes and ovaries, but with male genitalia due to the production of testosterone by a faulty adrenal gland. This condition can be corrected surgically and with hormone treatments. After treatment, the baby will anatomically grow to be a normal healthy female and will also be able to have children. These cases illustrate the difficulty in defining sex by the chromosomes an individual possesses.

Since the 1960s, sex tests have been used in athletics to prevent males from competing as females. Sex tests before 1968 consisted of visual inspection of external genitalia. However, at the Mexico City Olympics a new test was employed, the Barr Body test. The Barr Body test is used to determine the presence of a second X chromosome. A few cells from the wall of the cheek can be used. These cells are stained and examined microscopically.

Despite evidence that sex determination was based on other factors aside from chromosomes, the test was used until 1992. Some women's athletic careers may have been undermined by this test. Starting at the 1992 Winter Olympics in Albertville, France, a new test was used to test for the presence of the *sry* gene. However, most scientists still do not believe there is a good test to determine sex. Many believe what is really being tested is testosterone levels. Testosterone can cause an increase in muscle mass. However, testosterone levels are independent of the *sry* gene. Consider the following: an XY female can have a mutation in the *sry* gene that renders the *sry* gene product nonfunctional. These individuals are women but are excluded from competing in athletic events. Some scientists believe that athletes should not be tested for their genetic sex. It is difficult to define sex tests that truly tell the difference between men and women. The test currently in use can be unfair to some women.

DEATH AND DNA

Control genes are powerful in sex determination and their effects are lifelong. Their effects last from conception through childhood, puberty, and into adulthood. Scientists have wondered if there are also controls on aging and death. Are these events preprogrammed in our genes? Over the past 100 years, the average life span of an individual has increased to about 75 years. In the same way that there are control genes that begin development, there may be genes that control aging. Cells may be programmed to divide a certain number of times and then die.

Werner's Syndrome is a genetic disease causing premature aging in individuals. Dr. Sydney Shall studies this disease at Sussex University in England. One possible hypothesis is that people affected by the disease have their aging clocks set faster than normal; this causes them to age faster. Dr. Shall has found that the mutation responsible for Werner's Syndrome affects the rate at which tissue can regenerate. Tissue is constantly regenerating in the body, in wound healing, for example.

Aging may be defined in two ways: by decay and damage to the brain and damage to the tissues of the rest of the body. Brain tissue is not able to regenerate itself, therefore the damage is permanent. The rest of the body's tissue can regenerate and replace damaged tissue.

Individuals affected by Werner's Syndrome cannot regenerate tissue fast enough. This explains why Werner's Syndrome patients do not have degeneration of brain tissue. Werner's Syndrome does not affect the brain; therefore, the Werner's gene is probably not the aging gene. But there is also evidence that aging is not predetermined by our genes at all. Dr. James Vaupel is trying to find out if there is a genetic time clock on life span. He knew people were living longer, but was there a limit on how old people can get? To find his answer, Dr. Vaupel went to Scandinavia to study mortality records. After studying the detailed Swedish records of older individuals from 1750 to 1950, Vaupel believed the upper limit to aging, if there is any, is well beyond 100 years of age. More and more people are living to see their 100th birthday.

LIVING LONGER

Vaupel found that prior to World War II, there were very few people living beyond 100 years of age. Since World War II, however, there have been more and more people living to 100 years and beyond. Vaupel estimates there are currently 30,000 people in the world above the age of 100 and this number doubles every seven to eight years. Dr. Vaupel also studied a unique archive of twin studies maintained since 1870 in Denmark. Examination of these files revealed that of the 50,000 identical twins, who, by definition, have exactly the same genes, most do not die at the same age, as one might expect if death is genetically predetermined. Vaupel does not believe there is a genetic clock with a predetermined time of death. The evidence appears to confirm there is not a genetic determination to aging and death. Many people view aging as another step of development, however, Vaupel does not believe his studies necessarily support that statement. Vaupel believes that children born today have a good chance of seeing their 100th birthdays. He also predicts a large increase in the elderly population during the next century.

There are 3.3 million people over the age of 85 in the United States. By the year 2080, officials predict 18.7 million, and this number could reach 72 million in 2080 if there is not a genetically predetermined age of death, as Dr. Vaupel believes. A population explosion of this sort could have serious social consequences.

The evidence so far indicates there are no death genes in our genetic instructions. Then how and why do organisms die? One intriguing example is the Pacific salmon, where one species may live for five years, while another has an average life span of only two years. Salmon hatch in mountain streams and immediately swim toward the ocean. In the ocean, the fish mature to adulthood. After years in the ocean, the salmon make their way back to the same spawning ground where they were hatched. Salmon then die after laying their eggs.

A SECONDARY ISSUE?

Reproduction, not death, is the important issue in biology. Once an individual has successfully reproduced it has guaranteed the continuation of the species. What happens to the individual following reproduction is, in evolutionary terms, irrelevant. Dr. James Kirkwood, a zoo veterinarian, studies aging and death in animals. Most animals in the wild are killed by predation, but in zoos they are protected from this hazard.

One of Kirkwood's animals is a 14-year-old South American marmoset. In evolutionary and genetic terms this animal has been a success: it has reproduced and passed on its genes to the next generation successfully. However, it is still living on. The animal is beginning to show signs of aging. Dr. Kirkwood expects this animal to eventually die of a degenerative disease, such as a tumor. The problems of old age are not the result of genes that cause aging, rather they are caused by the harmful genes that negatively affect post–reproduction-age individuals. Harmful genes that affect individuals before reproduction have, to a great extent, been eliminated by evolution. These genes must be mostly eliminated in order for a species to survive. However, there is no selection against the harmful genes that affect us after reproduction. The products of these genes accumulate and result in symptoms of aging and eventually death. Examples are the genes causing heart disease and cancer. They are responsible for the majority of deaths in older individuals.

Mortality usually strikes individuals when their parents die. Whatever evolution's intentions, aging senior citizens are a cultural resource of wisdom and experience. It is through language, not genes, that this information is passed on through the generations. It is inevitable that our parents, as well as ourselves, will eventually succumb to the processes of aging and death. However, through the mechanisms of evolution, our parents' genes, as well as our own, will be passed on to the next generation. Our ability to communicate and pass on knowledge and experience further increases this genetic immortality.

Genes affect our lives, from conception through death. Genes are immortal because they are passed from one generation to the next. In effect, our parents live on in us because we have their genes and we will live on because we have given our children our genes. The study of our genes may or may not allow us to extend our life spans, but in an evolutionary sense we are already immortal.

Organisms by Design

JOHN F. KALINICH AND MAX FOGIEL

GENETIC CHIMERAS

Genetic engineers have the capability to change the natural order of things. For instance, genetic engineers can alter the genetic makeup of a tomato. But what exactly have they done to alter the tomato, and is the tomato still a tomato? Biotechnology may give scientists the power to revolutionize medicine and investors the opportunity to profit from this success. The benefits seem clear, but some people caution that this new technology may also bring new concerns.

Nature has always had a particular order to it. What type of organism an embryo will divide and grow into is determined by the genes it carries. Mice pass on mouse genes to their offspring and humans pass on the genes that make them uniquely human. But current scientific techniques and knowledge have given researchers the tools to transfer genes from one organism to another. The genes of a human can be put into pigs, the genes of fish into tomatoes, or elephant genes into mice. The era of organisms by design has begun.

Some of the sheep currently grazing on the hills of Scotland do not, as one might expect, belong to farmers, but are owned by a biotechnology company. They regard these sheep in two ways. First they see a profit for investors who have provided the funds for the research that has led to the creation of these sheep.

Second, this is a good scientific idea put into practice successfully. The ability of scientists to manipulate nature in this way raises many ethical questions. Some people believe that scientists are overstepping their bounds when manipulating nature in this way. They argue that since everything is not known about the natural order of life, life should not be altered by humans.

These sheep peacefully grazing in Scotland look and act the same as normal sheep. However these sheep can be worth $10,000 or more. What makes them so valuable to scientists and investors, and so ethically questionable to their critics, is the presence of a human gene in their normal genetic make-up.

MYTHOLOGY BECOMES REALITY

Chimeras are creatures that are part human and part animal. Historically, humans have always been fascinated by this type of creature. For example, the centaur, a figure in Greek mythology, is part horse and part man. This idea of a combination of human and animal is still with us in modern mythology: Dracula, the combination of man and bat, or the werewolf, a combination of man and wolf.

Although the examples given are fictional, genetic chimeras do exist. Since the discovery that DNA is the genetic material, scientists have learned a lot about how the instructions for making an organism work. Genes from any species can now be isolated and transplanted into any other species. This scientific fact has now been transformed into an industry built on the power of this new technology.

Children in the eighth grade are learning the techniques of biotechnology. The tools of science are easily manipulated. Experiments can be conducted by these students because of the recent discoveries made in the field. The students can even learn to transfer a gene from one organism into another. Bacteria are used in biotechnology to carry foreign genes. The bacteria used is a common bacteria, *Escherichia coli,* which is normally found in the digestive systems of humans, but is grown in the laboratory in special containers.

The bacteria are harvested by scooping them up with a wire and transferring them to a test tube. DNA is added to this test tube containing the bacteria. This mixture is cooled, heated and then cooled again. This is the procedure for transferring genes. The DNA used could be from any species and does not have to be bacterial in origin. The bacteria grow for a day, after which time the foreign DNA has been incorporated by some of the bacteria. Bacteria are able to recognize the foreign gene and carry out its instructions. In order for the bacteria to do this, the usual DNA to RNA to protein pathway is followed. The foreign gene is first transcribed into ribonucleic acid, or RNA. The RNA acts as a messenger to bridge the gap between the information encoded for in the DNA and the final manifestation of this information, the proteins in the cell. After being transcribed from DNA, the RNA is translated into a protein by the cell. The DNA is left intact by this procedure and reforms its normal double helix structure. If the genes transferred into the bacteria are of human origin, then the bacteria begin to produce human proteins. In this way, human proteins, including those that may be used as drugs, can be produced in large quantities.

TRANSGENIC ANIMALS "LITTLE FURRY FACTORIES?"

October 14, 1981 was an historical first for scientists and investors alike. It was on this day that biotechnology gained the financial backing of investors on Wall Street. Within the first hour of trading, the value of the new biotechnology stock had tripled. Since then, many billions of dollars have been invested in hundreds of new biotechnology companies. Each of these companies offers the opportunity to produce human proteins that may have therapeutic value in certain medical conditions, including heart attacks, strokes, diabetes, and cancer. Although the investment has been great, the results have been very slow in coming. One of the problems is moving from an experimental scale on the laboratory bench to the large factory production line where huge amounts of materials are needed. This process can be time-consuming and costly.

The problem is creating an artificial system to do what organisms do every day, but on a much larger scale. One biotechnology company takes a different approach. Instead of recreating the living factory with plastic and steel, they are using the living animal. Living animals are then used as factories to produce large amounts of human proteins.

Milk is a good source of expressed human proteins. Blood and urine are other sources of expressed human proteins; however, milk can be harvested easily and large quantities can made daily. Casein is the primary protein found in milk. The gene for casein provided the genetic "on" switch for milk-specific expression of foreign genes. The casein gene is expressed only in milk. The gene has specific elements in the DNA found before the start of the gene. It is these elements that will turn on the gene's expression.

Researchers have manipulated the casein gene in the following manner: first, they put the genetic "on" switch, found in front of the casein gene, at the beginning of a human gene. The next step was to put this new gene back in the genetic material of an experimental animal model, for example, a mouse.

THE TRANSFER OF GENETIC MATERIAL

The transfer of the genetically altered material into a new organism begins with the fertilized egg. The DNA must be surgically inserted into the egg. The fertilized egg at this stage of development is so small that the surgery must be done with the use of a microscope. First, the egg is held in place by a suction tool, then the DNA is injected via a needle, finer than a hair, into the single cell. The needle is inserted through the outer membrane of the egg and into the nucleus. Each egg must be injected individually and then checked for the presence of the genetically engineered piece of DNA.

The eggs are implanted into a surrogate mother and, after the embryos develop, mice are born. These mice are checked for the presence of the engineered gene. Only a few of the hundreds of mice injected contain the gene. In order for the gene to be expressed, it must be taken up by the DNA of the fertilized egg and the gene product produced in the milk. Mice are then checked for the presence of the gene product in their milk. Mice that produced the human gene product in their milk are considered successfully engineered.

Although the amounts of human protein produced by these mice were not large, researchers had proved the idea workable. This was the first step in developing a process. In order to produce a large quantity of material, the mouse is not an ideal organism because of its size. The mice would not produce the quantities of milk needed for mass production. Dairy animals are used by scientists because they produce large amounts of milk.

Some researchers went to Frank Loew of Tufts University Veterinary School. Dr. Loew saw this new technology as an opportunity to revive a sluggish dairy economy. This new technology offered a new use for dairy animals. Goats were chosen because they reproduce twice as fast as cows and produce large quantities of milk.

Karl Ebert, a colleague of Dr. Loew's, works on the expression of a protein that would be used to treat heart attack patients. The process of expressing this gene is the same in principle as that used in the mice. The gene that is transferred into the animal of choice is called the transgene and the animal which incorporates the gene into its own DNA and expresses the gene product is called the transgenic animal.

THE POTENTIAL FOR PROFIT

The human gene being transplanted into goats is used to treat heart attacks and works by dissolving blood clots. This drug is potentially worth millions of dollars. Each dose would cost more than one thousand dollars. The hope is that each transgenic goat would produce millions of dollars worth of protein in its milk. The scientists must test each baby goat born to see if it contains the engineered DNA. But first, the kids must be born. Even animals that could potentially be worth millions of dollars can have a difficult time during the birthing process; therefore, veterinarians make a concerted effort to save every animal. The kids may be very valuable and are taken from their mothers immediately after birth. They are hand-fed so as to minimize any risk of passing disease from mother to baby. The kids are then tested for the presence of the gene. As yet, transgenic goats that express this clot-busting gene have not been produced. Dr. Loew and his team continue to try to produce these transgenic animals, although it is a long and difficult process.

TRANSGENIC MICE

Transgenic mice can be engineered to produce huge quantities of foreign protein. This technology was developed by John Clark in Edinburgh, Scotland. The technology is similar in principle to the techniques used in making transgenic mice and goats in earlier examples, however, Clark made some significant improvements.

After testing several hundred mice to see if they contained the transgene, in June of 1990, Clark found one mouse that not only contained the gene, but was expressing it in huge quantities. This technology has been applied to sheep. A new biotechnology company was founded on the principles of John Clark's mouse. The proteins that the company hopes to commercialize are Factor-9, a protein used to treat hemophilia, and AAT, a protein used in the treatment of a deadly lung disease. Some sheep are producing 30 grams of AAT per liter of milk.

The choice of expressing human proteins in sheep's milk was an excellent one. The sheep have been called "little furry factories." They are capable of making a lot of product; 30 grams of AAT is worth more than one thousand dollars. The sheep are making product and doing so for little money. These transgenic sheep are worth hundreds of thousands of dollars and are zealously protected by the biotechnology company that owns them. The transgenic sheep are mixed in with many other normal sheep. Only the company knows which are the valuable sheep, producing therapeutic protein, and which are producing normal milk.

Got Milk?

Robert Boyd and Joan B. Silk

GOT MILK?

All mammals feed their young milk ... and all milk is a mixture of water, fats, proteins, sugars, and sprinklings of various minerals, vitamins, and hormones. The proportions of those ingredients vary greatly from species, to species. Sheep milk, for example, is about 80 percent water, 9 percent fat, and 5 percent protein; the milk of the great blue whale is 50 percent water, 30 percent fat, and 12 percent protein. Infants, as might be expected, do best on the milk of their species. This much biologists have known for a very long time, but they did not even suspect how milk composition related to parenting styles until Devorah Ben Shaul, an Israeli biologist employed by the Jerusalem Biblical Zoo in the 1950s and '60s, began pondering some unusual findings.

Ben Shaul became interested in milk and its composition because she often had to hand-rear wild animals and wanted to be able to concoct solutions that would simulate an infant's normal diet. In order to do this, she needed to know what that diet was. So she set out to collect and analyze samples of milk from hundreds of wild animals—humpback whales, Arabian camels, hippopotamuses, water shrews, water buffalo, one dead spiny anteater, and almost everything in between.

"I expected, of course, that the major correlations could be made on the basis of species relationship," Ben Shaul wrote in her groundbreaking paper in the *International Zoo Yearbook* in 1962, "but [I] soon found that this was not so. I found myself confronted with irrational results such as the fact that a grizzly bear and a kangaroo had virtually the same milk composition or, as another example, the reindeer and the lion."

Some researchers might have been tempted to put these findings away in a drawer, to chalk them up to contaminated glassware or an incompetent technician, but Ben Shaul persevered. As the number of her samples grew, she began to see a pattern—a connection between the composition of an animal's milk and its nursing behavior. Perhaps, after all, it made sense, that the milk of a grizzly bear and a kangaroo should be so similar, since in both species mothers are always with their young and the young can nurse at any time. The milk of both is very dilute compared with that of many other animals. It consists of about 88.9 percent water, 3.0 percent fat, and 3.8 percent protein.

Dogs, cats, and rodents, by contrast, all have milk that is more concentrated and higher in fat. But they all leave their young in nests for hours at a time, so perhaps that also makes sense. Fat, after all, has the highest satisfy value of any food. Goats, sheep, and primates, whose young follow or are carried by their mothers at all times, have, like grizzlies and kangaroos, milk that is relatively dilute and low in fat ...

In the decades since Ben Shaul's paper was published, her data on milk composition have been augmented and refined with samples from many more animals and from animals at different points in their lactation periods, but her basic insight has stood. It has been used to explain even more bizarre nursing phenomena than those of which she was aware. Kangaroos, for example, have since been found to express very different types of milk from their two teats. One type, a low-fat variety, is for the newly born kangaroo, that embryonic-like thing that will be a permanent resident of the pouch for many months. The second type, a higher-fat brand, is for the young-at-foot, a joey that is old enough to leave the pouch but will continue to suckle for five to eight months, putting its head inside the pouch to do so. What is most astonishing is that a kangaroo mother can express these two types of milk at the same time. She can nourish both a young-at-foot and a pouch baby. The joey is always sure to drink from the correct tap because its embryonic sibling is actually attached to its teat (by its mouth) and will be for some time.

In her original paper on the rationale of milk composition, Ben Shaul also recognized that milk can reflect factors in addition to child care, factors relating to the ecology of a species, to the environment in which it lives and how it lives in that environment. The high-fat milk of whales, seals, and dolphins, she pointed out, is a result of the fact that these animals spend a good portion of their time in cold water. Since then, bats, mammals in whom flight has placed a premium on weight reduction, have been found to have milk that is high in fat and dry matter but very low in water. Primates have been found to have milk high in carbohydrates because carbohydrates are necessary for the rapid brain growth that primate young experience after birth. Animals whose brains are almost completely developed at birth—seals, for instance—have milk that is very low in carbohydrates.

Seals also provide a striking example of just how intimate the connection is between milk composition and the environment. Small ringed seals, for instance, give birth on the fast, permanent ice of the Arctic seas, and mothers nurse their infants for two months on milk that is about 45 percent fat. By contrast, hooded seals (also known as crested or bladdernose seals because of black sacs on top of the males' heads) give birth on the impermanent sea ice of the North Atlantic regions. Because their cradle is always in danger of being broken up by storms, currents, or warm weather, these animals have the shortest lactation period of any mammal, just four days, but their milk is the richest of that of any mammal, more than 60 percent fat. During the four days that hooded seal infants spend with their mothers, they nurse frequently, about every half hour, and put on about fifteen pounds per day.

Milk is some kind of miracle brew all right, carefully concocted to meet the physiological needs of the young in the environment in which they are raised; concocted, too, to reflect how a mother takes care of her young, whether she is a nester, cacher, carrier, or follower, as biologists have dubbed some of Ben Shaul's groups. The nutritional needs of infants and the feeding styles of mothers evolved together to produce, for each species, a finely tuned solution of proteins, vitamins, fats, minerals, and carbohydrates. An infant best grows and thrives on its particular solution, and improper growth—or consequences even more severe—results when infants are fed on the milk of almost any other species.

Not long after Ben Shaul published her findings, researchers began to wonder what, if anything, the composition of human milk could tell us about humans, about the circumstances in which humans evolved and the way human infants first suckled.

Nicholas Blurton Jones, an English ethologist, was one of the first to look at this question, and he began by simplifying Ben Shaul's categories. He divided terrestrial mothers into just two basic types: continuous feeders, mothers who carry or are followed by their young and are, therefore, in constant contact with them, and spaced feeders, mothers who cache their young or keep them in nests. These two groups, as Blurton Jones pointed out, differ in certain predictable ways. Spaced feeders, as their name implies, feed their young at widely spaced intervals, and their milk has a high protein and fat content; also, their infants suckle at a rapid rate. Continuous feeders, on the other hand, carriers like primates, marsupials, and certain bats, as well as followers like sheep and goats, feed their young more or less continuously, and their milk is low in fat and protein; their infants suckle slowly.

So where do humans fit in this scheme? With a fat content of 4.2 percent and a protein content of 0.9 percent, human milk clearly puts us in the category of continuous feeders. This fits in well with what we know of infant care in the few remaining hunter-gatherer societies, the !Kung of the Kalahari Desert or the Papua New Guineans, whose mothers carry their infants (on their hips or in a sling) and nurse them very frequently (during the day as often as every fifteen minutes, and at night at least once until they are about three years old). It also makes sense of some of the idiosyncrasies of the modern human infant's behavior, such as the fact that a crying baby is quieted by rocking movements in the range of sixty cycles per minute, just the speed of a human female as she walks slowly, looking for food, perhaps, and carrying an infant on her hip. Or the fact that today's infant is noisy, in sharp contrast to the silence of most primate babies. The wailing that we've come to expect from our infants may not always have been part of their behavior pattern. Infants who are in constant skin-to-skin contact with their mothers rarely get so hungry that they cry for food. Their mothers are able to read their early hunger signals—moving, gurgling, fretting—and help their infants to the breast long before they get to the point of crying.

Colic, too, may be the result of treating our continuously feeding infants as if they were spaced feeders. When hand-reared rhesus monkeys are fed on a two-hour schedule, they vomit and burp frequently, something that rhesus monkeys fed by their mothers never do. "Perhaps the frequent vomiting and 'posseting' of human babies is a result of our insistence on the very early development of a four-hourly schedule rather than the quarter-hour and two-hour interval suggested by comparative data on milk composition," Blurton Jones has observed.

Blurton Jones is probably right, yet it is so easy to see how this change might have come about, how women, even women who loved their infants dearly, must have leapt at the opportunity to put their babies down for a while in some safe spot—a house, a bed, the care of an older sibling—and go about their business unimpeded. It is easy to see how they might have stretched the nursing interval, not to the point where the infant's health and growth obviously suffered and milk production was curtailed but to some point where the infant continued to thrive *and* the mother had a little time to herself. Baboon mothers would certainly understand this. It is the nature of every lactating female as she juggles her needs and the needs of her infant. It is the same balancing act that has led to crèches and aunting behavior, baby-sitters and communal nursing.

The Human Brain

SARAH R. RIEDMAN

When you look at a sliver of spleen or liver tissue under a microscope, you can't tell whether it came from the top, bottom, right or left side of the organ. That is because these organs have the same kind of tissue in all their parts. So if you know what the tissue in one part of an organ does—what kinds of stuff it makes—you know what the rest of the organ does.

For at least two thousand years everybody believed that the brain was different, that not every part of the brain did the same thing as every other part. With one part of it people saw, with another part they heard, with still another part they moved. But no one had tried to prove this until Franz Joseph Gall, an Austrian doctor, who was born in 1758 and died in 1828, took to puzzling about it.

Gall was in the habit of studying the shape of people's heads. He noticed that some were long and flat, some high and pointed; some had high, wide foreheads, and others had narrow, low ones. In some people the part around the eyes bulged, while in others the temples were prominent. Gall reasoned that if different parts of the brain did different things, then a person who had a good imagination and was, for instance, a good story teller, might have that part of his brain better developed. If a man used his hands well in making things, another part of his brain would be larger. If any part of the brain grew more than another, this would show in a growth of that part of the skull, as if it were pushed out by the brain. Gall's study of the skulls of people who had special mental ability of one kind or another went on for many years. He was very much in earnest about this idea, and he tried to make others believe it.

One man in particular, Cesare Lombroso, born in Italy eight years after Gall's death, believed in the theory and through it achieved international prominence that lasted well

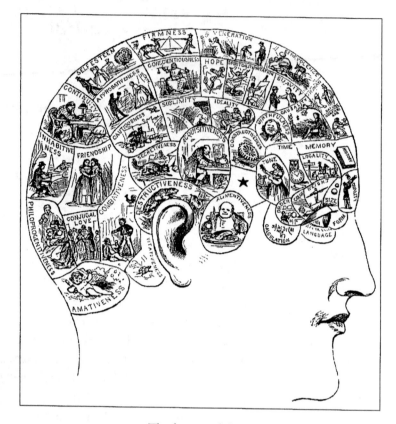

The human brain

into the twentieth century. Lombroso, a criminologist who was professor of medical law at Turin, claimed that there was a born criminal type, that a criminal could be distinguished by the shape of his head.

Unfortunately, a good idea is sometimes overworked, not only honestly as by Lombroso, but in a distorted fashion. In fact, some people make a business of it. Many quacks and fakers, who lived during and after Gall's time, began to make money from people who believed that their characters and fortunes could be told by an examination of their skulls. The business made so much money that it has continued even up to our own time. This pseudo-science was (and is) called phrenology. Today, people who believe in fortune-telling through tea leaves and palm-reading still pay good money to have their skulls "read."

PEOPLE AND PIGEONS

Gall was not all wrong; different areas of the brain do control different functions, and where a particular function is better developed, so is that part of the brain. This was an important conception—that the brain was not simply one organ but many organs in one. So while Gall himself was not to be blamed for the interpretations of the phrenologists, people did begin to neglect the scientific parts of his idea.

Meanwhile, while Gall was teaching in Paris, a Frenchman, Marie Jean Pierre Flourens, did a different type of experiment. Piece by piece, he removed the upper part of the brain (called the *cerebrum*) of a pigeon and found that when he removed a small part, beginning with the front end, the pigeon recovered from the operation without missing the part much. But when he removed all of one cerebral hemisphere, the pigeon became blind in the eye on the opposite side. When both hemispheres were removed, the bird became totally blind. Removal of the cerebellum (a part of the brain behind and below the cerebrum) left sight, hearing, standing and walking intact, but the animal lost its power to fly with the beautifully coordinated movement of a normal bird. Flourens' work, repeated by Magendie, threw into the discard Gall's notions of a many-organed brain. However, scientists were ready to believe the equally exaggerated, but opposite, idea that all parts of the brain did about the same thing.

This was not true. Flourens had made one important error: man is not a pigeon, and a pigeon's brain is no match for a man's brain. Flourens was right about pigeons, but he had no evidence that men's brains worked the same way. It is as if a scientist, working on the stomach, found that chickens have a crop in which food is mixed with swallowed pebbles, and decided that people must be that way, too. Birds and human beings, and especially their brains, are too different for such comparisons to be very safe. Later, as we shall see, much more fruitful experiments were done with the brains of dogs, monkeys and apes, animals which are much closer to man.

FERRIER MAPS THE BRAIN

Often one type of experiment will not show the truth quite so easily as another. Forty years after Flourens, in 1870, two German doctors tried a different kind of experiment, which proved more exact. Gustav Theodor Fritsch and Eduard Hitzig opened the skull of a dog so that the brain could be plainly seen. They placed a live electric wire on one side of it, and, much to their surprise, found that the muscles on the other side of the dog's body twitched. The dog was asleep under ether and certainly could not move its legs by itself. Every time they repeated this stimulation the muscles moved. They were correct in calling this part of the brain the motor area, meaning the part of the brain which starts the muscles off.

By this time, a brain specialist had already noticed that a different part of the brain, up in front, was the special part controlling speech. He found that patients who had forgotten how to speak had something wrong with that part of their brain. It was always the same part.

Then in the last quarter of the nineteenth century, a British doctor named David Ferrier, who was especially interested in illnesses of the brain, set to work to find out more about how it worked. He decided to experiment with an ape. The ape, he said, was more like man than was the dog. Using the same method as Fritsch and Hitzig, he set himself the job of finding out about all parts of the brain. Like an explorer, he made a map of the parts he charted in his explorations. Not only did he discover that the motor area started the muscles off, but that a small part of that area would make one set of muscles move but not another, the top of the brain, when stimulated, made the toes and feet wiggle. The next section down made the legs twitch, while the next one moved the muscles of the back. Then came the part for the arms, then for the face. His chart was like an orderly map of the parts of the brain controlling each part of the body from head to foot—with the top controlling the feet and the bottom the face.

At will, he could now stimulate with an electric current one area or another of the brain and get the different parts of the body to move. He also found that it was always the right side of the brain which controlled the left side of the body. But Ferrier now found that the brain does more than just start muscles off—it also has special parts for seeing, hearing, and feeling: the eyes, the ears, and the nerves in the skin connect up with a special central switch in the brain. The brain, therefore, is an organ of many centers.

Was Gall right, then, and Flourens all wrong? Not entirely. Flourens came fairly close to the truth (of course he might have been wrong since he was mostly following a hunch). The only way to make sure was to experiment; and this David Ferrier did.

When we put together everything we have learned from experiments and illnesses of the brain, there seems to be some truth in both ideas—Gall's and Flourens'. True enough, the brain, unlike the liver, is a many-centered organ, with different parts that do special jobs. But the parts also work together in making interpretations and judgments and in reasoning. If one little part of the brain is injured, it may keep the whole brain from working. For the whole brain to work properly, each of the parts has to work properly, too.

Why? Here's a very simple example. If we think about eating a chocolate ice cream cone, we remember how it tastes, smells, looks and feels. It takes at least five brain centers to do this—one for tasting, one for smelling, one for looking, one for feeling the ice cream's coldness and wetness, and one for the actual eating. And all of them together give us the idea of eating an ice-cream cone. If such a simple thing as thinking about eating ice cream uses so many parts of our brains, what about solving a problem in mathematics, or driving a car?

The Evolution of Skin Color

SARAH R. RIEDMAN

What events took place in the evolution of our species that led to such dramatic differences in skin color across the world? Comparing humans at different latitudes and with other primates suggests that there have been several major shifts in skin pigmentation during the past 6 million years or so of human evolution. Most of the skin of living primates is unpigmented except for exposed areas not covered with hair, suggesting a primitive feature in primates from which our ancestors changed. The best model for our own ape-like ancestors is probably the condition found in living chimpanzees, which have lightly pigmented skin covered with dark hair. As hominids adapted to the tropical savanna, the density of body hair most likely decreased and the density of sweat glands increased, both leading to a relatively naked skin best adapted for heat stress. As such, the hair no longer provided protection against the potentially harmful effects of UV radiation, and skin color most likely darkened as a selective response (Jablonski and Chaplin 2000).

Until almost 2 million years ago, all hominids lived in Africa and presumably had dark skin. As early humans expanded out of Africa into parts of Asia and Europe, they moved into northern latitudes with less UV radiation. The present-day distribution of human skin color suggests that, over time, populations living farther away from the equator become increasingly lighter. This distribution raises two basic questions: (1) why specifically is dark skin more adaptive at or near the equator? (2) Why did skin color become lighter farther away from the equator? Can the same factor be responsible for both, or did different selective factors operate at different latitudes?

SELECTION FOR DARK SKIN

Several models have been proposed to explain the evolution of dark skin in human populations at or near the equator, all linked to the greater amount of UV radiation found in that part of the world. The common element of these models is that dark skin acts as a natural "built-in" sunscreen (Jablonski and Chaplin 2002,75).

Sunburn

UV radiation can cause severe damage to unprotected skin. The most immediate effect is sunburn. While we have a tendency to think of sunburn as a temporary, although painful, nuisance, severe sunburn can have major consequences. Severs sunburn can damage the sweat glands, which in turn can have a negative impact in a person's ability to handle heat stress (Byard 1981, Jablonski and Chaplin 2000). Given the fact that hominids first evolved in a tropical environment, the problem of heat stress may have been particularly acute if, as we expect, the transition to savanna life included a reduction in hair density and the increased production of sweat glands. Under these conditions, light-skinned individuals prone to sunburn and damaged sweat glands would be at a disadvantage and would be selected against. According to this scenario, dark skin appeared in the first hominids as an adaptive response to protect against UV radiation damage to sweat glands. Another consequence of severe sunburn is an increase in infection to damaged skin cells (Byard 1981, Rees and Flanagan 1999, Jablonski and Chaplin 2000), which could also influence relative survival and render light-skinned individuals at a disadvantage. It seems reasonable to suggest that darker skin evolved near the equator at least partially as a means of protecting against UV radiation damage.

Skin Cancer

Damage to the skin due to UV radiation over extended periods of time can lead to skin cancer, brought about by UV radiation damage to a gene that normally inhibits cancerous growths. The risk of developing skin cancer varies among human populations by as much as 100-fold, a difference that appears to be strongly related to skin color (Rees and Flanagan 1999). There are two lines of evidence that link skin color, UV radiation, and skin cancer rates. First, there is a strong correlation of skin cancer incidence and mortality with latitude, with both decreasing with greater distance from the equator. Second, skin cancer rates are lower in darker-skinned populations than lighter-skinned populations at the same latitude. In Texas, for example, the incidence of nonmelanoma skin cancer is 5 per 100,000 among nonwhite residents compared to 133 per 100,000 among white residents (Bell and Steegmann 2000).

Given these data, one suggestion for the evolution of dark skin in humans living at or near the equator is that light-skinned individuals would be selected against due to increased susceptibility to skin cancer. It has been argued, however, that skin cancer is unlikely to have been a significant factor in The Evolution of Skin Color because cancer tends to occur later in life, often after the reproductive year (Jablonski and Chaplin 2000). Since natural selection operates through differential survival and reproduction, any disease influencing survival after the reproductive years would not be subject to natural selection. Other argue that while the incidence of skin cancer among younger individuals may be lower, it is still sufficient for the action of natural selection. Robins (1991) compared skin cancer rates among albinos and nonalbinos in Africa. Since albinos lack any pigment, they are more subject to skin cancer. All of the albinos showed skin cancer or premalignant lesions by the age of 20, suggesting early onset, at least in this sample. Skin cancer might have been a factor in the evolution of dark skin among our ancestors, although it was probably not the only factor. Rees and Flanagan (1999) suggest that although skin cancer was a likely factor in the evolution of dark skin in the tropics, risks related to severe sunburn were probably more important.

Vitamin D Toxicity

Vitamin D is an essential nutrient for humans. With the exception of fatty fish, such as salmon, most foods are generally low in vitamin D. In the United States, we are used to associating vitamin D with milk, but in this case the vitamin had been added to the milk during processing; cow's milk is generally low in vitamin D. Most vitamin D in humans is obtained from a biochemical synthesis in the skin brought about by the action of UV-B (wavelengths between 280 and 320 nm), which converts 7-dehydrocholesterol into a substance known as previtamin D, which then converts to vitamin D (Robins 1991).

Too little vitamin D can cause a variety of problems, as discussed below. In terms of the adaptive value of dark skin under high UV radiation levels, Loomis (1967) suggests that dark skin evolved to prevent toxic effects of producing too much vitamin D. High dosages of vitamin D are sometimes administered to people suffering from vitamin D deficiency, and in some cases an overdose can result in toxic levels of vitamin D, which can lead to excess calcium absorption, kidney failure, and death (Robins 1991). Loomis (1967) argues that dark skin prevents up to 95% of the UV radiation from reaching the deep layers of the skin, where vitamin D is synthesized.

While logical, this hypothesis must be rejected given measurements that show that humans do not synthesize toxic levels of vitamin D. Holick et al. (1981) examined the effect of artificial UV light on skin samples from light- and dark-skinned humans in order to determine the rate of previtamin D synthesis. They found that synthesis of previtamin D increases only up to a certain level, after which it remains at a plateau. After this point, 7-dehydrocholesterol converts into two inert substances rather than previtamin D. Therefore, vitamin D toxicity due to UV radiation is not possible, and the hypothesis is rejected.

Folate photolysis

Several nutrients are subject to photolysis, chemical decomposition brought about by visible light. One such nutrient, folate (a compound belonging to the vitamin B complex group), has been implicated in the evolution of dark skin. Branda and Eaton (1978) found that folate concentrations in human blood plasma decreased significantly after brief exposure to UV light. In order to show that the same effect occurs in living humans, they further compared serum folate levels in 10 light-skinned patients who were undergoing therapeutic exposure to UV radiation with 64 healthy light-skinned people. The patients undergoing UV exposure had significantly lower serum folate leves than the controls, suggesting photolysis.

Branda and Eaton (1978) suggest that light-skinned individuals are likely to show folate deficiency in environments with high levels of UV radiation. Jablonski and Chaplin (2000, 2002) note that folate deficiency is clearly linked to differential survival and fertility. There is a link between folate deficiency and the incidence of neural tube defects, congenital malformations that affect the development of the nervous system. Two of these malformations, anencephalus and spina bifida, are more common in light-skinned populations and account for a notable percentage of infant deaths. It is also worth noting that Africans and African Americans with darker skin show lower levels of folate deficiency and neural tube defects. Folic acid prevents 70% of neural tube defects, and it seems reasonable to assume that low levels of folate can predispose individuals to neural tube defects during development of the embryo. Jablonski and Chapin (2000, 2002) also note that there is a link between folate deficiency and differential fertility. Several studies have shown that induced folate deficiency leads to problems in sperm production and increased incidence of male infertility.

According to Jablonski and Chaplin (2000, 2002), folate photolysis was the major factor in the evolution of dark skin among early hominids in equatorial Africa. Those with lighter skin would be more likely to suffer from the photodestruction of folate, thus leading to increased mortality due to increased incidence of neural tube defects and decreased fertility due to the increased incidence of male infertility. Light-skinned individuals would thus be selected against because of differences in both survival and reproduction, while those with darker skin would be selected for because of the protective effect of dark skin on folate photolysis.

The folate photolysis hypothesis is supported by epidemiological and physiological data, and it seems reasonable to assume that folate deficiency was the major force shaping the evolution of dark skin in equatorial hominids. This does not mean, however, that other factors, such as sunburn and skin cancer, did not also influence overall fitness. Dark skin protects against UV radiation damage, which in turn can include both nutrient photolysis and damage to the skin and sweat glands.

SELECTION FOR LIGHT SKIN

The available evidence suggest a protective role of dark skin against the damaging effects of UV radiation in populations at or near the equator. The current distribution of human skin color shows that human populations that moved away from the equator, particularly those that moved far to the north, evolved lighter skin. The potential damage from UV radiation decreases as one moves away from the equator, but this means only that lighter skin could evolve; it does not explain why it did. To fully explain the current distribution of human skin color, we need a way to explain why light skin is found at distances farther from the equator. We can rule out random genetic drift since it is extremely unlikely that random variation in skin color in the absence of selection would lead to the observed high correlation of skin color and latitude.

Vitamin D Deficiency

The most widely accepted model for the evolution of light skin focuses on the role of insufficient UV radiation. UV radiation declines with increasing distance from the equator. This change means that the potential damage due to UV radiation also decreases, as shown by studies of latitudinal differences in skin cancer rates, among other findings reviewed above. For light skin to be favored in such environments, however, it is necessary to consider problems in survival and/or reproduction that would result from receiving too little UV radiation. Specifically, the idea here is that darker skin would be selected against (and hence lighter skin selected for) because reduced UV radiation leads to a deficiency in the production of vitamin D.

Loomis (1967) noted that nontropical regions receive low amounts of UV radiation during the year and suggested that individuals with dark skin would be at a selective disadvantage because they would suffer from a deficiency in vitamin D synthesis. The main effect of vitamin D deficiency is the childhood disease rickets, the defective growth of bone tissue. Severe rickets can obviously lead to reduced fitness, particularly given the active hunting and gathering life of our ancestors. Further, rickets can directly impact on differences in reproduction when pelvic bones are deformed during growth, thus leading to later complications and possible death during childbirth. The area of the pelvic inlet in women with rickets is only 56% that of healthy women, suggesting a greater incidence of difficulties during childbirth. Studies in the 1950s, performed prior the increased use of vitamin supplements, showed that African American women had a much higher incidence of a deformed pelvis (15%) compared to European American women (2%) (Frisancho 1993). This suggests, but does not prove, a relationship with skin color as we must consider other genetic and/or environmental differences between the two ethnic groups. Nonetheless, this ethnic difference is consistent with the vitamin D deficiency hypothesis.

Dark skin reduces the amount of vitamin D synthesis, and it takes longer for previtamin D synthesis in dark skin. Holick et al. (1981) measured the rate of previtamin D synthesis in skin samples exposed to the same amount of UV radiation as found at the equator and found that it took 30–45 minutes for lightly pigmented skin to reach a maximal level and 3–3.5 hours for dark skin to reach a maximal level. These findings support the vitamin D deficiency hypothesis, which argues that dark-skinned individuals would be at a selective disadvantage outside of the tropics.

Not everyone agrees. Robins (1991) argues against the vitamin D deficiency hypothesis. He notes that rickets is a disease that come about in more recent times, with the spread of civilization and cities, and tends to be found in polluted cities but to be rare in rural areas. Robins (1991) also notes that vitamin D can be stored in body tissues, allowing people at synthesize enough vitamin D during part of the year (summer) to last through times of lower UV radiation (winter). Also, while dark-skinned individuals are less effective at synthesizing vitamin D, they are still capable of producing enough even at higher latitudes to allow survival. Robins's main argument here is the differences in vitamin D synthesis between light- and dark-skinned people are relative, and the reduced rate of synthesis in the latter would not pose a selective disadvantage. He cites several studies suggesting that, outside of polluted urban areas, dark-skinned people would be able to produce enough vitamin D. As further evidence, Robins also points out that there is little evidence of rickets in skeletons from preindustrial Europe, raising the question of whether rickets was present in sufficient degree to constitute a selective factor. Others have contested Robins's arguments, noting that the evidence for high levels of vitamin D storage is lacking (Frisancho 1993). Beall and Stegman (2000) note that skeletal analysis of rickets focuses on the most severe manifestations of low vitamin D levels, and lower values might also have biomedical significance. Finally, Jablonski and Chaplin (2000) analyzed UV radiation levels across the planet to estimate the expected levels of previtamin D at different latitudes. Their analyses support the vitamin D deficiency hypothesis by showing that medium and dark skin would be at a disadvantage at higher latitudes, being less likely to be able to synthesize adequate levels of vitamin D.

Cold Injury

While many anthropologists have accepted the vitamin D deficiency hypothesis as the most likely explanation for the evolution of light skin, others have suggested the variation in temperature might also have an impact (Post et al. (1975). The cold injury hypothesis proposes that heavily pigmented skin is more susceptible to damage, such as frostbite, and would therefore be selected against in cold environments. Since average annual temperature tends to vary with latitude (hottest near the equator), this model further suggests that observed correlation of skin color and latitude actually reflects, to some extent, an underlying correlation with temperature (recall from Chapter 10 that latitude is often used as a proxy for temperature in studies of human adaptation).

There is some statistical evidence for the influence of temperature on skin color variation. Roberts and Kahlon (1976) found that annual temperature was significantly related to skin reflectance even after variation in latitude was taken into account. More direct support for the cold injury hypothesis comes from medical records of soldiers, particularly during the Korean War, where winter conditions were severe. For example Ethiopian troops, primarily dark-skinned, had the highest rates of frostbite of all nationalities, with rates almost three time times that of the U.S. forces. This comparison is crude because the U.S. forces included both white and black soldiers. However, comparisons within the U.S. forces showed that frostbite among blacks was between four and six times that among whites, even after controlling for other factors (Post et al. (1975).

Physiological studies also suggest a relationship between pigmentation and susceptibility to cold injury. Post et al. (1975) cite a number of examples, including studies of piebald guinea pigs (having black and white–spotted skin). They froze black and white areas of the skin of anesthetized guinea pigs and found that cold damage was more severe in the darker skin. Cold injury was always more severe in the pigmented skin of the guinea pigs.

While some scientists have accepted the plausibility of the cold injury hypothesis (e.g., Robins 1991), others have not. Beall and Stegman (2000) argue that black–white differences in cold injury might instead be due to known differences in the vascular response to cold and have nothing directly to do with variation in pigmentation. In other words, the cold injury hypothesis may be based on a spurious correlation. They also suggest that the guinea pig experiments are not directly relevant to human cold injury, primarily because the temperatures used on the guinea pigs were more extreme than typically found in likely human environments. Instead, they make the case, as do Jablonski and Chaplin (2000) that light skin evolved in response to vitamin D deficiency. Of course, these two models are not mutually exclusive. It is possible that both vitamin D deficiency and cold injury contributed to the evolution of light skin farther away from the equator. Although the evidence supporting the vitamin D hypothesis is strong, this does not preclude the possibility that differential cold injury was also a contributing factor. As is often the case in evolution, one's overall fitness reflects the net effect of phenotypic response in a given environment.

Sexual Selection

Another model also considers the evolution of light skin to be a consequence of past natural selection, but instead of relating light skin to environmental variation, this model rests upon the concept of sexual selection. First developed by Charles Darwin, sexual selection occurs when there is competition for mates or where there are preferences for mating with members the opposite sex that have certain physical characteristics (Aoki 2002). A classic example of the latter is the preference of females in a number of species of birds and fish to choose brightly colored males as mates. Given this preference, there would be an advantage to having bright coloration, and any genes underlying this coloration would be selected for over time.

The sexual selection hypothesis as applied to human skin color rests on the assumption that human males prefer females with lighter skin color. Aoki (2002) suggests that if this assumption is correct, then the present-day geographic distribution of human skin color could be explained by a balance between natural selection and sexual selection. His model suggests that natural selection tends to favor darker skin but that (as discussed above) the intensity of this selection diminishes with increasing distance from the equator. Consequently, any preference for lighter-skinned mates would have its greatest impact when the counteracting natural selection for dark skin is lowest; that is, farther away from the equator. Aoki's model represents a balance between selection for dark skin and (sexual) selection for light skin.

What is the link between a preference for light skin and selection? Jones (1996) suggests that given a tendency for female skin color to darken with age, lighter skin might have acted as a signal for greater fecundity. However, this connection has not been demonstrated, and as noted earlier, the relationship between skin color and age varies even among closely related groups (Williams-Blangero and Blangero 1991).

Although the sexual selection model seems reasonable, it rests upon the critical assumption that there was widespread preference for light skin in past human populations. Van den Berghe and Frost (1986) performed a cross-cultural analysis of ethnographic accounts and found preferences for light skin color in mates in 47 out of 51 societies, with males expressing this preference more often. There remains the question of whether these preferences, recorded for recent human societies, apply to our past as well. In other words, is a preference for light skin part of our species' evolutionary history, or does it represent the widespread adoption of culturally based preferences, particularly standards spread via colonialism? Although some authors argue that a preference for light skin existed historically throughout much of the world prior to European colonialism (Jones 1996, Aoki 2002), we of course have no evidence regarding mating preferences from earlier historic or prehistoric times. Perhaps the major problem with the sexual selection hypothesis is showing a link between mating preference and mating behavior. The hypothesis would be strengthened with a demonstration that mating preferences have a significant impact on the actual choice of a mate. Although the sexual selection hypothesis has its proponents (e.g., Aoki 2002), other anthropologists feel that although sexual selection is perhaps a contributing factor, the evolution of light skin has been affected more by the link between UV radiation and vitamin D production (e.g., Jablonksi and Chaplin 2002).

No Selection?

Another view on the evolution of light skin is that there is no selective advantage for light skin, either through natural selection or sexual selection. Brace (2000) and Brace and Montagu (1977) have argued that when humans moved farther away from the equator, selection for dark skin decreased. Over time, mutations for light skin arose; and in the absence of selection against them, these neutral mutations became more common. The underlying assumption in this model is that any mutations would interfere with the production of melanin and therefore lead to lighter skin.

Although this neutral mutation model has not received much support, the idea that light skin may not reflect a selective advantage has resurfaced with Harding et al.'s (2000) analysis of the MC1R gene. Using statistical methods to detect past natural selection from genetic diversity measures, they found evidence for strong selection in Africa but a lack of evidence for selection in European populations. Instead, they argue that patterns of MC1R diversity in Europe are consistent with neutral expectations, suggesting a lack of significant selection for light skin. However, other analyses of MC1R diversity do suggest a selective interpretation (Rana et al. 1999). In addition, it is not clear to what extent variation (and selection) for the MC1R gene is related to variation and selection in skin color. Variation in MC1R explains only part of the variation in skin color, and it is possible that other genes affecting skin color are influenced by adaptation (Harding et al. 2000).

What Is Sex For?

JAMES H. MIELKE, LYLE W. KONIGSBERG AND JOHN H. RELETHFORD

N atural selection is like a meticulous accountant. If the benefits of doing things in a particular fashion outweigh the costs, no matter by how little, the way of doing things will be favoured. We know that sexual reproduction imposes an enormous cost on females, the cost of producing sons, which halves the return on a sexual female's investment. There are other costs too. So it is reasonable to ask what sorts of benefits there might to be offset those costs. If we can identify the benefits we will be well pleased at having solved this particular puzzle, but we may discover that in some cases there are no counterbalancing benefits; in those species sex is barely hanging on. A shift to asexual reproduction could easily vanquish it.

One of the commonest arguments is that sex exists because it enables evolution to go much faster. This it does by enabling favourable mutations to be combined together in a single body and spread through the population. In an asexual species favourable mutations can only accumulate in the descendants of one clone, while sex will bring them together from different individuals. This is an attractive argument, one that we have already dealt with by comparing a sexual to an asexual bacterium. There we showed that the sexual species would probably do better because it could become resistant to two antibiotics more quickly than an asexual species could. In fact, we were cheating with that example, because the bacteria have such vast populations that any mutation would be almost certain to arise relatively quickly. (If sex did make a difference to bacteria, they would use it far more often than they do). That is the biggest problem with this particular argument; to get a difference between the sexual and asexual groups, the size of the sexual group needs to be large enough so that the mutations are indeed present in two different organisms. If the population is small, then the sexual population, like the asexual, will simply have to wait for the new mutation to arise, and by the time this has happened the first favourable mutation will have spread through the whole population anyway. As a rough rule of thumb, the population needs to be about ten times 'larger' than the chance of some mutation happening, the population would need to be about 10 million for sex to make any difference to the speed at which favourable mutations would accumulate. And that seems a little unlikely.

This is one problem with the 'go-faster' explanation of sex. There is another. As we have said, recombination is a double-edged sword. What sex brings together, it will also break apart. Recombination allows new sets of genes to be offered up to natural selection; it also ensures that those sets will be broken up the next time they are sexually shuffled. If you have a winning combination, how much better simply to copy it by cloning.

Another aspect to this kind of explanation of sex is one that considers the effects of sex on a whole lineage of related organisms. Because sex allows for variety, it enables species to respond to environmental change more readily than if they were asexual. That means that organisms with sex are more likely to evolve into different species then organisms without sex. Asexual species are likely to go extinct rather than branch. So the overwhelming preponderance of sex might be a reflection of the better survival and evolutionary branching of groups that can perform sex.

These two arguments, that sex enables faster evolution and that it promotes speciation, are the most common explanations. We have hinted at some of the difficulties, and will return to them, but first we should note that they both take a very long-term view. Sex is seen as advantageous in evolutionary time, even through it loses out in the short term. That may be so, but can we not find advantages in the here and now?

George Williams, at Stony Brook, has adopted a straightforward approach to the problem of sex. [8] He takes as his starting point the observation that many life forms alternate between sexual and asexual reproduction. They may reproduce by cloning for many 'generations' but they then indulge in a bout of sex. The aphids that infest rose bushes are like this. The females who arrive on the bush grow genetically identical clones within themselves, and those daughters may already be growing granddaughters before they are even born, three generations supported by one efficient set of mouth parts and the rose's supply of food. But then come the winter, a change in the environment, the female aphids produce winged males and females, which mate sexually and lay eggs. Or think of strawberry plants, which cover the ground by spreading asexually produced plantlets on the ends of runners, but also produce flowers that set sexually produced seeds. Williams argues that there must be some mutation that would be capable of suppressing the sexual stage completely, and that if this were to save the organism the costs of sex then it would spread very quickly.

The common dandelion is a simple example. Dandelions do not reproduce sexually, but produce seeds which carry the same genetic message as the parent, and, indeed, as each other. Dandelions come in a few varieties, descended from sexual ancestors, but today the members of most of those varieties are no more than clones. Out of more than 2000 species of dandelion only 50 reproduce sexually and they are restricted to small regions of West and Central Asia and the Mediterranean. The dandelion can hardly be regarded as an unsuccessful plant, as any gardener struggling to keep a patch of lawn free of them will testify. Nor is it restricted in where it will grow; members of one clone are found as far afield as Greenland and Florida. But the dandelion's success does not, today, depend on sexual reproduction. If conditions changed—if a new Ice Age rolled across the Northern Hemisphere, perhaps—then dandelions might feel the pinch, losing the habitats in which they thrive and being unable to adapt to the changing conditions. Then, sex could be advantageous; but today, as far as the vast majority of dandelions are concerned, it is not worth it.

This example also throws another sidelight on evolution, worth a slight detour from our main argument. If dandelions do not reproduce sexually, they have no need for pollination and no need to attract insects to carry their pollen from flower to flower. Yet one of the most distinctive things about the dandelion is its bring yellow-orange flower. What can it be for? Quite simply, it serves no purpose, but is a reminder that the dandelion is descended from sexual ancestors. Many generations ago bright flowers to attract insect pollinators and ensure reproduction were essential to those ancestors. But once a genetic pattern becomes fixed in a line that reproduces without sex, evolution goes so slowly that, for all practical purposes, it ceases in that line. Mutations are so rare that there is no realistic prospect of eliminating the waste of resources involved in the production of those attractive, but useless, flowers. The first mutant dandelion to reproduce asexually (which probably arose quite recently) had insect-attracting flowers, and so all dandelions today have coloured flowers, whether they need them or not. In this case the advantages of asexual reproduction, even with the useless appendage of a bright yellow flower, obviously outweigh the disadvantages of sex. But the very fact that so many organisms continue to use sex point to a powerful short-term advantage, one that at least matches, and perhaps exceeds, the two-fold advantage of cloning.

The aphid's life gives an insight into what advantage of sex might be. A rose bush is a hugely abundant source of food. Any aphids that happen to land on it will be up to their ears in food. They will reproduce, each as fast as it can, and slowly the fastest growing clone will edge the others out by sheer force of numbers. That clone will be the winner of the race to exploit that rose bush, and it is the winner because it is more perfectly adapted to the exact conditions on that rose bush than any of the other aphids who happened to land there. But when the resources represented by that particular rose bush have been exhausted, it will be time to send out pioneers to seek new sites. The successful clone has two options. She can send out lots of identical clones, in the hope that one of them will land on a rose bush exactly like the exhausted one, where its genetic endowment will ensure a measure of success. Or she can send her investment out in the form of several slightly different variants, the products of sexual reproduction, in the hope that one of them will land on a rose bush to which it is perfectly suited. The strategy that will play best will be dictated by the likelihood of finding an identical rose bush. If the chances are good, send out the clones. (Which, of course, is what she does while filling a particular rose bush with her offspring.) But if the pioneers are likely to find themselves in a different environment, then it is probably better to make each slightly different and hope that, in the race to exhaust a fresh source of supply, your offspring, despite being only half yours, is the one that is ideally suited to that supply.

It is in this context that Williams developed his oft-quoted analogy of the lottery. Asexual reproduction is like buying a whole stack of identical lottery tickets; if that number is a winner, you will be a winner. Sexual reproduction is buying half as many tickets, but each with a different number; if the winning number is uncertain this gives you a better chance than a stack of Xerox copies. Williams went on to apply this type of thinking to a diversity of different lifestyles, not simply the aphid.

The strawberry, for example, cannot move freely about within the resource as the aphid can, but it can spread and hop to colonise new lands. The strawberry plant spreads by making clonal copies of itself, and these will continue to spread as long as they are better adapted than neighbouring clones, which are probably different. In this way the strawberry clone will come to cover that part of the habitat that it is best adapted to. Rather than the discrete spatial boundaries that limit the aphid's spread, it is shifts in environmental conditions that limit the strawberry's growth. When it comes to long-distance spread, however, the strawberry is in exactly the same position as the aphid. The environment that a seed finds itself in is most unlikely to be identical to the environment it come from, so variation among offspring gives the strawberry the best chance of establishing further successful clones elsewhere.

Another case that Williams examines is the one he calls the elm-oyster model. Here, the problem is that hundreds or even thousands of juveniles can occupy the space that will eventually be taken up by just one adult. Oyster larvae are minute compared to the full-grown adult, and the carpet of seedling below an elm gives just a hint of the competition between them to become established. An elm seedling may find itself with no competition for a while, but as it grows it will come under the influence of neighbouring seedlings that are also growing. The more successful will crowd out the less, eventually killing them, and will continue to grow. As they do so they come into contact with yet more seedlings, and the competition now is tougher because those seedlings too have won small local competitions. The cost of meiosis is just one small factor buried beneath all that extra selection. The eventual winner has had to conquer thousands of rivals in order to grow to maturity, and a variety of different competitors is the best way to ensure that one of them might win.

Because the prize is finite—only one elm can occupy the space—there is nothing to be gained from having multiple copies of the winning genotype. Neither elm nor oyster ever reproduces asexually. They are exclusively sexual, and it is the fierce competition between juveniles that makes them so.

It is not simply the unpredictability of the environment that makes the new combinations afforded by sex successful. Nor is it the competition between different species. If that were so, we should expect to find a preponderance of sexual reproduction among species that are good at colonizing new areas, whereas in face many weeds are asexual. Rather, it is the competition between siblings. If each offspring went to a different new patch, sex and cloning would be equivalent, but because several offspring usually end up in the same patch, the parents are far better off with variety between their pioneers, so that in each patch there is a better chance that some new combination of their genes with another individual's will be the winner.

Williams considers three different types of reproduction systems that involve sex: the aphid alternates a bout of asexual multiplications with a sexual generation; the strawberry spreads across short distances with clones, but uses sex to go further afield; and the elm does not use clonal reproduction at all, but produces millions of seeds. These models can each be seen as extensions of an idea Williams called the sisyphean genotype. Sisyphus is the character in Greek mythology who laboriously pushes a boulder to the top of a hill. Just as he reaches the summit, the boulder crashes down the hill and he has to begin his labour again. Williams' point is that the fittest individuals, those best able to reproduce under the prevailing circumstances, would owe their success to a rather fortuitous combination of genes, and that combination would probably not be among the elite in the next generation. Hence, the sisyphean genotype has to be recombined anew in every generation, just as Sisyphus had to keep rolling his stone up the hill.

Each of his examples is a Sisyphus of a sort, trying to make at least a contribution to the most successful individuals of the next generation. The common factor in all is what Williams calls a very high level of zygote-to-zygote increase, or ZZI. (The ZZI is the number of offspring that a single organism is capable of producing; in species that alternate sexual and asexual reproduction it is the number of offspring produced sexually by all the clonal descendants of the original individual.) To give you an idea of what 'very high' means, consider not the aphid but the water flea, or *Daphnia*, which has a very similar life cycle. The growing season, during which the animals reproduce asexually, lasts about six months, and during its six-week lifespan an average female will produce about 40 young.

At the end of the growing season *Daphnia* lays eggs that will survive the winter and will be capable of sexual reproduction. If all the asexual offspring were to survive and reproduce, by the end of the season a single zygote could produce more than 10 million offspring. A female oyster over her lifetime may produce at least 100 million young. In every case where there seems to be an advantage to sex, it is because of the intense competition for resources between the offspring of a single individual. Indeed, most of Williams' mathematical models simply will not work if there are not enough offspring to compete, and that brings us to a major problem; many living things, perhaps all the ones that interest us, and certainly our own species, do not have nearly enough offspring. Competition between siblings is not strong enough to take evolutionary advantage of the variety that sex affords. They would be far better off, according to the mathematical model, putting the same effort into twice as many asexual offspring.

The world's most fertile woman, according to the *Guinness Book of Records*, had 69 children, at least 67 of which survived infancy. Even so, that is so far below the numbers needed by Williams' model as to be absurd. If competition for resources were the only factor, very few animals, and especially not the exceedingly slow-breeding human animal, would be sexual. Williams' conclusion is that 'sex must be disadvantageous' in 'mammals, birds and many insects'. The clear implication is that these species must have evolved from an ancestor that enjoyed very high fecundity and in whom sexual reproduction completely ousted asexual. For birds and mammals (and reptiles and amphibians too) that ancestor might have been a fish, or it might have been even older, a protochordate. As we shall see, where the ability to reproduce asexually has arisen in one of these low-fecundity species, it is generally exclusive; the clonal form is very successful and leaves no room for a sexual phase. One can conclude that human sex today is very definitely maladaptive, but then why has natural selection not been able to eliminate it?

The answer is that, as a result of many millions of years of evolution when sex was advantageous, there are now formidable obstacles that prevent its loss. One is that most organisms have completely lost the ability to bud off whole new versions of themselves. This is not quite so true of plants, which retain unspecialized cells that can form the basis of a new, physically separate but genetically identical individual, and is probably one reason why a return to asexual reproduction is quite common among low-fecundity plants. But animals, by and large, are not able to bud off clones, because as the zygote develops into the adult the cells become specialised and differentiated into the various tissues of the adult. Even those cells that continue to proliferate madly, like the cells that completely renew the lining of your gut every forty-eight hours, are trapped by their fate, able to produce endless quantities of new gut cells but not cells that will in turn develop into new individuals.

The exception, of course, is the embryo itself. Before development has proceeded too far it is quite capable of dividing into two or more parts that will grow into wholes. This is cloning, pure and simple, and it is very good for the embryo. A genome that finds itself in an egg that forms twins has effectively doubled its chances. But it does the mother no good at all. She has already paid the price of meiosis, and genetically identical offspring incur the costs of asexual reproduction without the benefits. The extra nutritional burden of twins may be one factor that discourages twinning, but especially in animals with large litters the added cost of a doubled embryo is not large. The benefit, to the embryo, is considerable. But despite the obvious imbalance in benefits between mother and embryo, the mother seems to win this struggle, and twinning is comparatively rare among mammals. Only armadillos go in for it on a regular basis. (Zygotes that find themselves in an egg provisioned with yolk presumably can seldom afford to build two offspring from a single supply of nourishment.)

Another obstacle to asexual reproduction is created by the very diploid that sex requires. Having two sets of genetic instructions means that a duff copy on one chromosome can be compensated for by a good copy on the other. The harmful recessive mutation will not be expressed, but nor will it be eliminated, so all diploid organisms carry an invisible genetic load of mutated stretches of code. If an animal chooses to become a haploid asexual, the harmful mutations will not be covered by a working copy of the gene, and so the offspring are liable to suffer very high mortality. Any opportunity to reconstitute the protective diploid state would be seized, and the organism would very quickly revert to being a normal sexual diploid.

The answer to this problem might he to stay diploid but reproduce asexually. The trouble with this option is that it seems to need a whole series of mutations to happen at the same time. Meiosis must be suppressed or cancelled in some way. The egg must resist fertilisation by sperm, which if it took place would almost certainly lead to an unworkable number of chromosomes. And the egg must be able to start and maintain its own development without either the signal provided by the sperm's entry or the mitotic spindle that the sperm usually provides. And yet despite the need for a seemingly impossible series of co-ordinated mutations, eggs do arise that are capable of parthenogenetic development, and one can artificially select for individuals in which parthenogenetic eggs have become quite common.

In fruitflies perhaps one in a thousand eggs will develop without being fertilised. Astute selection can increase this figure to more than one in 17, but only if the females are kept apart from males.[12] Were the female flies allowed to mate, the six per cent of eggs that are capable of unaided development would probably be killed by the addition of the male's chromosomes. Turkeys too can be selected for parthenogenesis. A strain was developed in which many unfertilised eggs showed some development, and one in several hundred reached maturity. Curiously, all the birds produced were male; that parthenogenetic females should give rise to males means that the offspring cannot be identical copies of their mother, though the exact details are not known.

Turkeys and fruitflies can be turned into asexual species, or at least made more asexual than they were before, but there are also, despite all the obstacles, quite a few vertebrate species that are predominantly asexual. (There are also many invertebrates without sex, but they will not concern us much here.) There are fish that have abandoned sex, though some of them retain a curious vestige of their sexual past, and amphibians too that multiply asexually. And in the southwest of northern America there is a flourishing group of lizards that reproduces entirely asexually. In none of these animals, however, is sexual reproduction an option; that is, these species are exclusively asexual and do not, like the aphid, have the option of using sex when they need to. Williams sees this fact as 'decisive evidence' that sex is a bad idea and would be selected against in practically all vertebrates. If it were not, sexual and asexual would be able to co-exist side by side.

Biologists recognise two main types of asexual reproduction in diploid organisms. One is called arrhenotoky, and involves producing males from unfertilised eggs and females in the usual way. It is common among social insects, where the special arrangement (males are haploid and females diploid) leads to odd kinship relations and a predisposition to become highly social. The other is called thelytoky, and is the production of females from unfertilised eggs. An egg can be made to develop into an adult female in two ways; either meiosis is entirely suppressed and the offspring is an identical copy of the parent, or else meiosis takes place but the reduction in chromosomes is made good by some special process. The first method, when there is no change in the genome, is called apomixes. The second is called automixis.

Apomixis is a fine method for producing identical offspring. If meiosis doesn't occur, the egg is effectively just a bit of the parent and will develop into an exact clone. Automixis, however, is more of a problem. The trouble is that no matter what steps are taken to overcome the halving of chromosomes during meiosis, the offspring will not be identical to the parent, and nor will they enjoy the protection of diploidy to the same extent. This is because crossing over and recombination after the duplication of the chromosome shuffle the mother's genes; if she now puts two sets of recombined chromosomes together in an egg, the chances are that some of the genes will have come originally from the same chromosome. The offspring will thus be homozygous for genes that the mother may have been heterozygous for. In the extreme case, when the mother simply duplicates one haploid set of chromosomes after meiosis, the offspring will immediately be homozygous at every locus. Whether it is all or just a few genes that are made homozygous, the result is that the offspring is exposed to all the dangers of the lethal recessive genes accumulated as part of the normal genetic load, and so it is most unlikely that an organism that has been reproducing sexually for some time will be able to give rise to viable offspring by automictic thelytoky. It can happen, but it is very rare indeed. Thelytoky with apomixis, by contrast, is relatively common.

Arrhenotoky will not lead to long-term asexual reproduction because the males are not themselves capable of laying eggs; but because it exposes the genes to selection in haploid bodies, it can pave the way for automictic thelytokous asexual reproduction by ensuring that the genome does not contain too many lethal recessive mutations. The few rare cases in which females produce daughters from unfertilised eggs that have none the less been through meiosis are each thought to be evolved from an arrhenotokous ancestor.

Theory, then, says that while asexual reproduction may be a highly desirable state of affairs for many animals, and probably all vertebrates, it is by no means easy to achieve.

A look at some of the species that have, as it were, gone back to their reproductive roots is very enlightening. One of the most interesting is a little fish called the Amazon molly (*Poecilia formosa*) which has almost, but not quite, done away with males. The Amazon molly is thought to have arisen from a hybrid of two closely related sexual species. It reproduces asexually sure enough, laying unfertilised eggs that grow into exact genetic replicas of the mother. Indeed, no male Amazon mollys have ever been found. But the females retain a curious reminder that their species was once sexual. In order to trigger the growth of the egg into a new clone, the egg must be penetrated by a sperm. And to get the necessary sperm the emancipated Amazon molly has to dupe a male of one of the closely related 'parental' species into mating with her. He gets absolutely nothing out of the deal; the genetic material in his sperm is totally ignored by the egg's genes. The molly has almost all the benefits of asexual reproduction, but still she has to find a male and get him to mate with her. Doubtless a female who could abandon even this last trace of erstwhile sexuality would do even better than her sisters. She would be able to explore territories where there were no males, for example, but there is scant chance of this happening, for the molly is now set in a rigid mould; having abandoned sexual reproduction she has also abandoned the chance of combining a new, 'sperm-free' mutation with the one that gave rise to her line, and will have to wait for such a rearrangement to happen to one of her descendants. Even so, and even bearing in mind that by human standards fish produce vast numbers of offspring, the Amazon molly has found it cost effective to abandon sexual reproduction.

The same need to find a male afflicts another of the asexual vertebrates, the salamander *Amblystoma*. Here again, there are two ordinary diploid sexual species, but two asexual types, probably the results of misguided mating. The parthenogenetic terms are triploid females, having a diploid set from one of the sexual species and a haploid set from the other, and like the Amazon molly they need to find a male and mate with him, for the eggs must be penetrated by a sperm before they will start to develop. It seems that the asexual salamander is slightly further down the road to complete female emancipation than the Amazon molly, because one does occasionally find all-female populations away from any males, and these are capable of parthenogenesis without even the minor mechanical stimulation provided by a sperm.

(There is an even more bizarre form of asexual reproduction in another fish, *Poecoliopsis*. As in *Amblystoma*, there are two completely normal diploid sexual species and a couple of parthenogenetic types that are triploid. But there are also diploid all-female types. These females mate with males, and the male genes are expressed in the offspring, but when the time comes for meiosis, only the female's genes go forward into the eggs.)

Parthenogenesis in vertebrates is paradoxical. If Williams' arguments about the benefits of sex are correct, asexual reproduction should be very common. But it is not. And yet, when it does occur, it seems to wipe sexual reproduction out completely. So the benefits of parthenogenesis are clear, and when it happens mere sex doesn't stand a chance. But the obstacles put up by eons of sexual evolution are formidable. Are those obstacles the only reason why asexual reproduction is rare? Perhaps not, for it is as well to remember that almost all our knowledge of evolution comes from fossils, and it is very difficult to tell how a fossil reproduced when it was alive. Williams was looking for a short-term advantage to sex. He found it, in the need to avoid competition between offspring. But if there is a long-term advantage to sex, one that, for example, helps a lineage to survive by making it more likely to give rise to new species, then we have another explanation for the rarity of asexual vertebrates. They are committing what Williams calls 'phylogenetic suicide'. Asexual reproduction may be a very good thing in the here and now, avoiding the two-fold cost of making males, but it may doom the species to an early extinction.

At any moment there may be literally hundreds of species that are on the verge of breaking through from sexual to asexual. For all we know human beings may be one such, and there may already have been true virgin births. When the breakthrough to asexual reproduction does occur, it spreads rapidly and wipes out the sexual ancestor. But without the long-term benefits of sex, the asexual species is prey to any sudden change in its circumstances. It is very vulnerable to extinction. Sexual species, by contrast, perhaps find it easier to adapt and so are more likely to survive, and more likely to branch. Thus the prevalence of sexual reproduction among the snapshot of species that grabs our attention now is not a reflection of the quick benefits of sex; those benefits accrue only to much more prolific multipliers. It is, rather, a reflection of the sad fact that asexual reproduction is better in the short-term, but doesn't last long. Hence, it doesn't often appear in a single frame from the movie of life. The prevalence of sex must therefore be either a hangover from earlier days or have something to do with long-term benefits (or both).

So far, we have mentioned two possible long-term benefits to sex. One is that it enables species to evolve more quickly, thus keeping up with changes in the environment. The other takes an even longer perspective and says that species with sex, because they can avoid extinction, give rise to new species more readily, and so groups that have sex will persist and proliferate. They may both be false. It is quite clear that sexual reproduction does indeed make it possible for a species to show almost limitless variability without any input either in the form of mutations or the arrival of related individuals adapted to slightly different conditions. Evolution is indeed faster with sex than without. George Williams, however, turns this observation on its head and asks why, then, evolution is so slow.

Bring an animal or plant into the laboratory and select for some character, and the species will respond very quickly. You can increase the number of bristles on a fruitfly, or the scent of a rose, in a very few generations. But look at the fossil record and it seems that species change only very slowly, certainly under natural selection they evolve at a rate much slower than they are capable of when man makes artificial selections. This could be because the environment simply does not require them to change more quickly, but if that were so they would abandon the evolutionary speed of sex for the increased returns of cloning. Or it could be because in the laboratory the scientist selects just one characteristic, and quickly uses up any genetic variability in that character, whereas in the wild natural selection acts on many things at once and has to balance the sifting out of variants against the creation of new ones by mutation. But either way the problem remains; if sex is good for fast evolution, why is evolution among sexual species so slow?

According to Williams, we are looking at the problem from the wrong end. Most biologists tend to think that extinction takes place when an animal cannot keep up with changes in the environment. Williams says that 'extinction occurs not because an organism loses its adaptation to an ecological niche, but because its niche becomes untenable.' The animal may be perfectly adapted to its niche, but the niche may vanish for other reasons. One example Williams mentions is the green turtle that nests on Ascension island in the middle of the South Atlantic. The adults feed on turtle grass off the coast of South and Central America, but every two years or so they make the monumental journey across the Atlantic to nest on Ascension. They are probably perfectly adapted to this life, and would continue to weather changes in, say, salinity, or currents, or nutrition. But if Ascension were to be eroded away that population of turtles, despite having the advantages of sex and recombination, would in all likelihood go extinct. 'If ... the island disappears,' Williams says, 'the last turtle to lay her eggs there may still be extremely well adapted to her niche, but it is a niche that in the next generation will permit a total of zero occupants.' [18]

In Williams' view, sex retards adaptation. The force of recombination that breaks up existing favourable hands is, he thinks, more important than that which brings new hands together. And this, so far from preventing evolution, enhances the survival of groups with sex. There are always a few oddballs out on the fringes who play the game slightly differently—the turtle who lays her eggs somewhere else, for example. When times change, the oddballs may survive while the main line goes extinct. Because sexual species do not go extinct as readily, they are more likely to speciate and give rise to farther sexual species. If organisms really did track the environment as quickly and as closely as they can in the laboratory, they could find themselves exquisitely well adapted to a way of life that is itself about to end, with no prospect of escape from the trap of overspecialisation.

It is very difficult to judge the merits of Williams' arguments as compared to the more orthodox view. It is appealling, true, but that is not enough. John Maynard Smith, of the University of Sussex, has developed mathematical models which show that under the right conditions sexual species certainly will change faster on the basis of existing variability, spread new mutations through the population more quickly, and follow changes in the environment more closely. But is that what keeps sex going in the long-term? We don't know.

There are just two more arguments about the long-term value of sex that we must deal with. They go by the name of Muller's ratchet and the Red Queen hypothesis.

Muller's ratchet comes from the geneticist H. J. Muller, who was one of the first to suggest, in the 1930s, that sex owes its existence to its ability to speed up evolution. Muller's ratchet is a more recent invention, dating to 1964. What he notes is that an asexual species can never get rid of harmful mutations. In that sense, mutations are like a ratchet; they can increase, but never decrease (except in the unlikely event of the mutation exactly reversing itself). A sexual species, however, because it can recombine genomes, has the opportunity to rid itself of bad genes. Occasionally offspring will contain as their new genetic hand a preponderance of harmful genes. They will die, but the species as a whole will do better because it will have filtered some of the harmful copies from the gene pool. Such a mechanism probably does work in the real world, especially where each genome is likely to experience less than one mutation during its lifetime, and where that mutation is not going to be very harmful. What Muller's ratchet really means is that any population will be able to replicate more DNA without accumulating errors if it uses sex and recombination than if it merely copies the DNA as faithfully as possible. More DNA, of course, means a potential for greater complexity. And the especially nice thing about this conclusion is that it brings us full circle. As John Maynard Smith explains, 'it is now widely accepted that the genes responsible for recombination evolved in the first place because of their role in DNA repair. What follows from Muller's argument is that recombination itself functions as a form of repair.'

So much for Muller's ratchet; it enables species to use sex to lift the pawl and rewind the ratchet. What of the Red Queen? It was the Red Queen who explained to Alice, in her adventures through the looking glass, that 'it takes all the running you can do, to keep in the same place.' To Leigh Van Valen, an evolutionist at the University of Chicago, this is a perfect analogy of evolution. Van Valen perceived a law in the fossil record, which was that any genus in a group, say any bony fish, seemed to have a constant probability of dying, going extinct, at any time. Van Valen explained that it was not the inanimate environment that was important but the living environment, the other species that share an area. Any change for the better in one of these species would automatically be a change for the worse for all the other species. If one species becomes a better competitor, the others are bound to suffer as a result. Hence, all species must evolve as fast as they can, just to stay on an even footing with all the others. Sex enables faster evolution, and so sex, like the Red Queen's frantic bursts of speed, is needed just to stay in the same place.

Between them, Muller's ratchet and Van Valen's Red Queen add yet further refinements to our knowledge of the costs and benefits of sex. Whether they are general phenomena, or apply only under certain stringent conditions, we cannot say. In common with most of the other models of sex we have looked at, they rely on changes in the environment to make sex worthwhile. But in mathematical models with realistic assumptions it is very hard to get these ideas to work, either because the population is too small or because the environment changes too slowly. Unsatisfactory though this is, in the short-term, it seems that sex can be a direct benefit to very prolific organisms whose offspring will compete among themselves for resources. In the longer term, sex may speed evolution and may also retard adaptation, both of which could promote the spread of sexual species at the expense of asexual species. But in the short-term asexual species, despite being doomed to an early evolutionary end, seem to win out in the battle with their sexual ancestors. All in all it seems that the business of creating a new individual from a mixture of two old individuals—for that is what sex is—is a remnant from earlier times.

Some species, like the Amazon molly, have managed to get rid of it. Human beings too might do better, in the sense of reproducing more effectively, if they could abandon sex (which means abandoning males), but that doesn't make it likely that we will undo all the biological inheritance and evolve away from sex.

Blood Pressure

L. L. LANGLEY

J ust as everyone learns early in life that his body temperature is supposed to remain constant, he also soon realizes that his blood pressure is supposed to remain constant. Perhaps we have a thermometer poked in our mouth, or elsewhere, more often because any parent can do that. But before long a physician will wrap a cuff around an arm, inflate it, affix his stethoscope, peer at a column of mercury on a meter, and by so doing he ascertains the blood pressure. Other than being an impressive ritual, there are good reasons for blood pressure determination. The reading is of value because normally, and throughout life, the blood pressure remains constant. It does so by virtue of superb homeostatic mechanisms.

First, what is pressure? The dictionary informs us that it is "any force which acts against an opposing force; a thrust, stress, or strain between opposed masses, uniformly distributed over the surfaces in contact as, steam pressure, the pressure of a gas in a confined space." Pressure can also be exerted by fluid. In this definition there are several important elements. Pressure is a force. This implies energy. Also, according to the above definition, there is an opposing force against which the pressure acts. Next, it is learned that the pressure is distributed evenly over the contact surfaces. And, finally, we have included fluid.

Putting all these elements together, the concept of blood pressure is easy to understand. The blood is a fluid. The heart provides the driving force. The opposing force is represented by the resistance to flow through a series of smaller and smaller vessels, and the force exerted is distributed evenly over the surfaces of the blood vessels.

Logically, then, any discussion of blood pressure must begin with a consideration of the heart. If the heart stops, blood pressure falls sharply, and death quickly follows.

The heart is a pump, and is so called in the vernacular. Hearts vary in different animal species. In lower forms, such as insects, the heart is little more than a tube of muscle interposed in the circulatory system. By simple periodic contractions it propels the blood in sufficient volume and pressure to meet the insect's needs.

In mammals, the heart is more complex. In man it consists of a muscular organ containing four chambers and a series of valves. It is really two pumps in one: a left pump and a right pump. The left pump is responsible for providing the force which drives the blood through the longer circulatory system. The right pump has a much less demanding role since it must drive blood only through the relatively short system of vessels that pass through the lungs. As the blood moves through the lungs, it takes up oxygen and gives off carbon dioxide. This oxygenated blood returns to the left side of the heart and is then circulated right side of the heart and is pumped through the lungs to complete the cycle.

If one looks at a two-sided heart it becomes immediately apparent that the left side is much stronger than the right. The left wall, which is mostly muscle, is many times thicker than the wall of the right side. Muscles grow in response to the work they must do and the left side must do far more work than the right. This adaptation of a muscle to the demands placed upon it may be looked upon as an important homeostatic development in itself.

The pressure in the shorter circulation, called the pulmonary circulation, is much lower than it is in the longer, or systemic circulation. When the physician determines blood pressure as described above, it is the pressure in the systemic circulation. Thus, the following discussion will principally concern systemic pressure, but mention will be made in the next chapter of the pulmonary circulation.

Returning again to the definition of pressure, we are reminded that the first element concerns the force. In the case of blood pressure, it is a driving force which is controlled by the heart. If there is no heart action there is no driving force. During exhaustive exercise, the driving force is maximal. Clearly, there is a range of forces which the heart can provide.

The normal heart in man, at rest, beats about 70 times per minute. This varies considerably. In the well-trained athlete, it is generally slower: 60 or even 50 beats per minute. One noted track star had a resting heart rate of 37 per minute! But the important consideration, for our purposes, is not how fast the heart beats but rather how much blood it can pump per unit time against the opposing force.

At rest, the normal left side of the heart in man, pumps between 5 and 6 liters of blood per minute. During heavy exercise that volume may be increased above 30 liters per minute. Here we are not concerned with the mechanisms that vary the output with exercise, but rather those that vary the output and thereby keep the blood pressure constant.

As has been amply demonstrated in previous chapters, in order to carry out such a function, the heart must be kept apprised of the blood pressure and of any change from normal. As is to be expected, there are sensors in the circulatory system which respond to changes in blood pressure. They then send messages to the brain which in turn can relay messages to the heart to change its function. The circulatory sensors, because they are

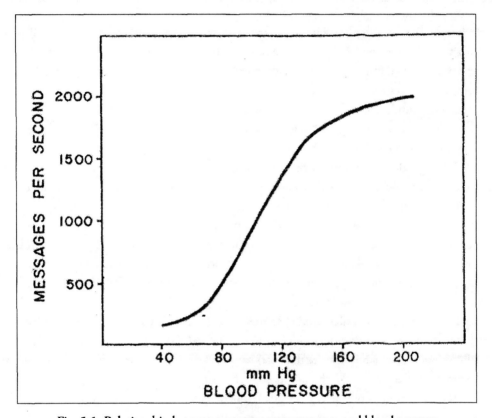

Fig. 5-1. Relationship between pressoreceptor response and blood pressure

As the blood pressure increases the arterial pressoreceptors fire more frequently. Note that the major change occurs between 80 and 140 mm Hg which is the normal range.

responsive to pressure changes, are called pressoreceptors.

Figure 5-1 shows that as the pressure rises the number of impulses (messages) sent to the brain per second increases. With each beat of the heart the pressure in the arteries varies from a low of about 80 mm Hg to a high of 120 mm Hg. The average arterial pressure, then, would be close to 100 mm Hg. In Fig. 5-1, it can be seen that 100 mm Hg is on the steep part of the curve which means that a slight change below or above that pressure markedly alters the number of impulses fired to the brain. It can also be seen that over a broad range, which extends from about 50 to 150 mm Hg, the pressoreceptors are responsive.

Next, it is necessary to understand how the messages from the pressoreceptors alter heart activity. Believe it or not, the heart can be removed from the body, and it will keep beating for a time. In fact, if certain precautions are taken, the heart can be kept beating outside the body seemingly indefinitely. A chicken heart continued to do so for 17 years and would have gone on longer if the laboratory attendant had not fouled things up! The point being made is that the heart, removed from all nervous influence, continues to beat at its own inherent rhythm. However, under normal conditions, the heart is supplied with two sets of nerves which can very definitely alter its function. One set speeds the heart and causes it to contract more vigorously; the other inhibits it thus decreasing the rate and force of contraction. These two sets of nerves may be likened to the accelerator and brake of an automobile. Actually, in the case of the heart, they are both active most all the time which is similar to driving with one foot on the brake and the other on the accelerator. Not very efficient in driving a car, but it works fine for the heart.

The left side of the normal heart in man, at rest, pumps about 80 ml of blood every time it beats. It beats about 70 times per minute, therefore 5600 ml of blood are ejected. Thus, the output per minute can be increased by increasing the heart rate, by increasing the amount of blood pumped during each beat, or by a combination of both. When the accelerator nerves are stimulated, the rate increases, and the force of contraction also is greater. Thus more blood per minute is pumped. The combination of more beats per minute and more blood per beat markedly increases the output. The converse is true when the inhibitory nerves dominate.

It should be now understood that there are sensors that monitor the blood pressure, that if the pressure increases, more impulses are fired to the brain, and as a result, the inhibitory nerves which innervate the heart cause a decreased volume of blood to be pumped per minute. Consequently, the blood pressure falls.

The definition of pressure, it will be recalled, states that a second important element is the opposing force. In the case of blood pressure this is provided in part by the tension of the blood vessel walls but more importantly by the resistance offered by the blood vessels to the flow of the blood

This principle is easy to understand. Take a garden hose, put a nozzle on one end, and hook up the other end to the faucet. Now open the faucet wide. Without actually measuring the pressure within the hose, everyone will agree that when the nozzle permits maximal outflow the pressure is lower than when the nozzle is closed so as to shut off the outflow. If the pressure were measured it would be found that when the nozzle is closed the pressure everywhere within the hose is the same and is equal to that of the house water pressure. On the other hand, as the nozzle is progressively opened and flow becomes greater and greater a gradient of pressures exists with the highest pressure at the end of the hose closest to the faucet and lowest at the nozzle end.

This analogy illustrates several basic and important principles. If there is a progressive decrease in pressure in the hose from one end to the other, it follows that the longer the hose the lower the output pressure. Secondly, it was stated that as the output flow is decreased by turning the nozzle, the hose pressure, at all points along the hose, increases.

These relationships were worked out over 100 years ago by the French physiologist, Poiseuille. The Poiseuille equation states that:

Pressure = flow × viscosity × length / radius

This equation simply says that the pressure is directly proportional to the flow of the liquid (blood), its viscosity, and the length of the tube; and it inversely to the 4th power of the radius. We have already discussed blood flow into the tube, that is, the blood vessels. It is a function of the heart. The viscosity of the blood generally remains constant; thus no further consideration of that factor is necessary, and the length of the tube (the blood vessels) does not change so it too needs no elaboration. However, the perceptive reader may think he has detected a contradiction because it was stated above that the longer the hose the lower the outlet pressure and the Poiseuille equation says that as the length increases the pressure rises. Actually, there is no conflict. If we use a short hose, measure the outlet pressure, and then add another length of hose, the pressure at that same point will be higher. It is higher because the added length of hose exerts resistance to the flow of water. But if the outlet pressure of the second length is now determined, it will be found to be lower than the outlet pressure of the first uncoupled hose.

The surprising factor in the Poiseuille equation is the inverse relationship between the pressure and the 4th power of the radius. Using the hose, it was seen that as the nozzle is closed the pressure increased. That is, as the outlet radius is decreased, the hose pressure is increased. It is also easy to demonstrate that the pressure varies with the 4th power of the radius. Since flow is usually easier to measure than pressure, let's rearrange the equation thusly:

Flow = pressure × radius / viscosity × length

Now we see that flow and radius are directly proportional. Take two glass tubes of the same length, but one with a radius twice that of the other. Hook them up through a Y-tube so that the driving pressure of water into each will be the same. Measure the outflow from each tube. You will find that when the outflow from the smaller tube is 1 ml the outflow from the larger is 16 ml (Fig. 5-2). This follows because the radius is larger by a factor of 2, and 2 to the 4th power is 16.

It may strike the reader that we have gone pretty far astray, but the principle is so important that careful explanation was thought necessary. The point is that because pressure changes with the 4th power of the radius of the tubes, small changes in the radius of the blood vessels will have an important effect on blood pressure.

Downstream from the arteries are smaller vessels called arterioles. As explained in Chapter Three, they are characterized by having a circular band of muscle. Contraction of this circular muscle decreases the radius of the vessel. Consequently, there is greater

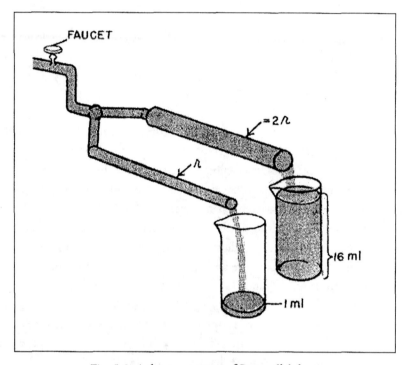

Fig. 5-2. A demonstration of Poiseuille's law.

Note that when the flow through the tube that is twice as large reaches 16 ml, the flow
through the smaller tube is only 1 ml. This is so because the resistance to flow is equal to
the 4th power of the radius.

resistance to the flow of blood through the constricted vessel and, according to the Poiseuille
relationships, the pressure upstream, that is, is the arteries, must increase.

Arterial pressure, then is controlled by two factors: (1) the flow which is determined by
the heart action, and (2) resistance to flow which is determiner by the arterioles. To put it
more simply, the pressure within the arteries depends upon the balances between the flow
of blood into the arteries and the flow of blood out of the arteries.

The feedback control of the heart has been discussed. There is also feedback control of
the arterioles. As explained in Chapter Three, there are nerves which regulate the radius
of these vessels, and as outlined above, there are sensors which monitor the arterial blood
pressure. The messages from these monitors go to the brain, and then information is sent
to the heart and also to the arterioles. Thus, if the arterial blood pressure rises, more messages go to the brain, the pumping of blood is decreased, and the radius of the arterioles
increases. This double barreled attack on the problem results in prompt, effective lowering
of blood pressure. In contradistinction, a fall in blood pressure causes increased heart
activity as well as vasoconstriction; blood pressure rises.

Just how important these homeostatic mechanisms are is dramatically shown when the
feedback system is destroyed. This may be done experimentally by cutting the nerves that

serve to transmit the messages from the pressoreceptors to the brain. Now if the animal is bled, there is a precipitous fall in blood pressure. After a loss of 10 percent of the blood volume, arterial pressure becomes too low to maintain life, and the animal will die unless prompt emergency steps are taken. In contrast, the animal with functional homeostatic mechanisms can survive a loss of about 40 percent of blood volume (Fig. 5-3).

Figure 5-3 also shows that, in the normal animal, there is very little drop in blood pressure as a result of moderate hemorrhage. This is due to the mechanisms described. If you have observed a person who has suffered significant blood loss, you will recall the very pale appearance, and if you had felt the pulse, it would certainly have been fast. In other words, the vessels were constricted in the skin as well as almost everywhere in the body except the brain, and the heart was beating fast and vigorously. As Fig. 5-3 reveals this suffices unless the blood loss is, indeed, very large. In view of the fact that the average persons has over 5 liters of blood, these figures indicate that they can survive the loss of a liter or two.

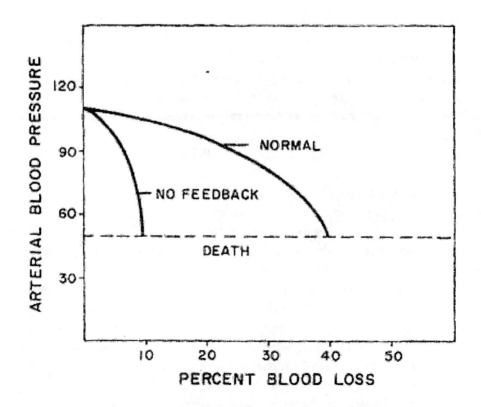

Fig. 5-3. The importance of homeostasis in hemorrhage

With the pressoreceptor feedback mechanism intact, a blood loss equal to 40 percent of the total blood volume may be tolerated. Without it, 10 percent may be fatal.

The blood pressure control systems are important not only in the rare event of hemorrhage but upon many other occasions as well. For example, take the simple act of getting out of bed. When one is upright, his circulatory system must contend with the force of gravity. Blood has to be pumped up from the heart to the brain, and blood must be moved from the legs and lower body up to the heart. On the other hand, gravity plays no role when one is in the horizontal position. Were it not for the blood pressure monitors, consciousness might well be lost upon assuming the upright position because gravity would sharply diminish the blood flow to the heart and to the brain. Note that the pressoreceptors which monitor blood pressure are located in the large vessels that carry blood to the brain. In other words, they stand guard at the entrance of the skull, and if the pressure is not up to snuff, they do something about it. They stimulate the heart and cause vasoconstriction elsewhere, and as a result, pressure rises sufficiently to overcome gravity and to assure uninterrupted blood supply at adequate pressure to the brain.

The influence of space travel on man has long concerned physiologists. It was thought that prolonged travel in a weightless environments would so lull the homeostatic control system that when one returned to earth there would be a dangerous drop in pressure. It would seem that we underestimated this system! Upon return to earth, adjustments are made rapidly, accurately, and effectively. Blood pressure remains within the normal range. Apparently, the control system is not easily lulled.

However, even under more mundane conditions, blood pressure does not always remain the same. During sleep it fails somewhat and during exercise it may double. These changes do not suggest a failure of homeostasis, but rather beneficial alterations. During sleep cellular metabolism is at its lowest ebb; demands are minimal, and therefore lower pressures suffice. As activity increases, however, cellular demands require more and more oxygen which is delivered by the blood. The rate of delivery is a function of the pressure. The greater the pressure the faster blood can be driven through the small vessels. Thus it is not surprising that when one runs a quarter mile flat out, blood pressure rises. The task of the physiologists is to ascertain the precise sequence of events that brings about this rise. To put it an other way, how does the circulatory system know it must deliver more blood, and once being informed, how does it do it?

Our purpose here is not to answer these questions but rather to indicate that the homeostatic system must either be inhibited or overwhelmed during exercise. It is functional, no question about that. As soon as exercise stops it range. The hypothalamus, here too, plays a dominant role. In an experimental animal, the hypothalamus can be stimulated and, as a result, all the expected circulatory changes consistent with exercise take place. It has been suggested back system so as to result in the increase in blood pressure. To be sure, the heart activity increases mightily, and there is almost complete vasoconstriction in all areas except the brain and the muscles. The result is that a large volume of blood is driven rapidly through the busy muscles.

Finally, as with any system, animate or inanimate, some thing sometimes goes wrong. The system may fail or be pressure, or, more commonly, high blood pressure. Yet, not too infrequently, blood pressure is homeostatically maintained perfectly for 60, 80, or even 100 years!

REFERENCES

Heymans, C., and E. Neil, "Reflexogenic Areas of the Cardiovascular System", Little, Brown, Boston, 1958.

Langley, L. L., "Outline of Physiology," 2d ed, McGraw-Hill, New York, 1965.

Rushmer, R. F., "Cardiovascular Dynamics," 2d ed., Saunders, Philadelphia. 1961.

Sarnoff S. J.and J H. Mitchell, "The Regulation of the Performance of the Heart," Am. J. Med. 30: 747–771, 1961.

Hadar, Lucy, and Laetoli

IAN TATTERSALL

W hile Richard Leakey's discoveries in the arid badlands of east Turkana were making his name a household word, a graduate student of Clark Howell's by the name of Donald Johanson was preparing for equal fame in an equally inhospitable environment several hundred miles to the north. Johanson had accompanied Howell to Ethiopia in 1970 and 1971, and through members of the Omo expedition's French contingent he eventually met Maurice Taieb, a geologist whose field area lay in the Afar Triangle of northeastern Ethiopia. At its northern end the great East African Rift Valley splits in two, one branch heading northeast into the Gulf of Aden, and the other northwest along the Red Sea. The Afar Triangle marks the spot where the three rifting systems come together, and Taieb was studying the geological evolution of this unusual "triple junction". During his surveys in the valley of the Awash River, Taieb had noticed rocks that he thought were probably Plio-Pleistocene, and which had abundant and well-preserved fossils eroding out of them. As a specialist in plate tectonics he wasn't interested in these fossils—but maybe Johanson was? Was he! Early in 1972, he joined Taieb and Yves Coppens on a brief survey of the Afar, and at a place called Hadar they found a paleontologist's paradise: desert badlands oozing fossils that seemed, by comparison with those from Omo, to be around 3 myr. Back in Addis Ababa, Ethiopia's capital, the three agreed to launch a full-scale joint expedition, which reached the field in the fall of 1973.

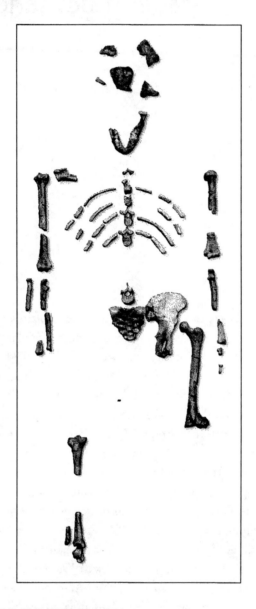

HADAR, LUCY, AND THE FIRST FAMILY

That first field season at Hadar produced a remarkable find among a large haul of mammal fossils: the distal (far) end of a femur, plus the proximal (near) end of a tibia, which together made up the knee joint of a small hominoid. Short of a pelvis, perhaps, a more telling piece of the body skeleton couldn't have been found. For the knee tells you a great deal about locomotion. In a quadruped—an ape, say—the feet are held quite far apart, and each hind leg descends straight to the ground beneath the hip socket. In bipedal humans, on the other hand, the feet pass close to each other during walking so that the body's center of gravity can move ahead in a straight line. If this didn't happen, the center of gravity would have to swing with each stride in a wide arc around the supporting leg—producing clumsy and inefficient movement and wasting a lot of energy. So in bipeds both femora angle inward from the joint to converge at the knee; the tibiae then descend straight to the ground. In the human knee joint this adaptation shows up in the angle—known as the "carrying angle"—that is formed between the long axes of the femur and tibia. The Hadar knee joint was clearly angled; and thus it was that, at the end of the field season, it was announced at a press conference in Addis Ababa that Hadar had yielded the knee joint of a bipedal hominid that had lived between 3 and 4 myr ago.

But this was merely a foretaste of what was to come. The next year, an enlarged group of researchers at Hadar discovered, first, some hominid upper and lower jaws, and then (drumroll ...) "Lucy." Lucy, as all the world came to know in a remarkably short time, is the skeleton of a young adult female hominid, reckoned by Johanson to be some 40 percent complete. She walked upright, as numerous details of her bony anatomy confirm, but stood only a little over three feet tall. Her skull is extremely fragmentary, but it clearly had contained a brain in the ape size range (though given her diminutive stature it was probably a little bigger in comparison to body size than an ape's). Her lower jaw is some-what V-shaped, and while her molar teeth are quite human-like, the front premolars are not bicuspid like ours. But what was most breath-taking about Lucy was the combination of her age and her completeness. Up to 1974, the earliest reasonably complete hominid skeletons known were those of Neanderthals, much closer relatives of *Homo sapiens* and all under 100 kyr old. As documentation of earlier stages in the evolution of the hominid body, only isolated bones were available. The only pre-Neanderthal hominid specimen that came even remotely close to Lucy in completeness was Broom's *Australopithecus africanus* pelvis from Sterkfontein, with its associated partial femur and some vertebrae. And while these remains were sufficient evidence on which to conclude that their owner had been bipedal, that was about all that could be said. Lucy, on the other hand, was complete enough to provide a pretty comprehensive picture of the kind of individual she had been. And she was also a good half-million years or more older than the fossil from Sterkfontein.

A year after the initial announcement of a 3-myr-old hominid from Hadar, then, Lucy provided clinching evidence to show that human precursors had indeed been up and walking on their hind legs at that remote point in time. But just what was Lucy? What species did she and the other Hadar fossils represent? Just before finding Lucy, Johanson had been visited in the field by Richard Leakey and other members of the Koobi Fora group. With modestly proportioned bony parts and a rather *Homo*-like balance in size between the incisor and molar teeth, the jaws that had already been found clearly did not belong to *Australopithecus boisei*, with its massive jawbones, tiny incisors, and massive chewing teeth. So Leakey, fresh from his discovery of ER 1470, quickly and predictably concluded that they must belong to an early species of *Homo*. By his own admission Johanson himself was already toying with this conclusion. On the other hand, it was clearly meaningless to consider the diminutive and tiny-brained Lucy as a member of our own genus. Thus, in their preliminary description in *Nature* of the 1973 and 1974 Hadar hominids, Johanson and Taieb concluded that two or three species were represented among them: a very primitive form of *Homo* in the shape of the isolated upper and lower jaws and, in the shape of Lucy and the 1973 knee joint, something else. Just what, exactly, remained to be determined, although Johanson and Taieb felt that these remains bore comparison with *Australopithecus africanus* from South Africa. And finally, they noted resemblances to robust *Australopithecus* in a temporal bone (part of the skull wall) that was found at the end of the 1973 field season.

The undoubted it as yet obscure importance of the Hagar hominids made it imperative to get them securely dated. To help with this task Johanson, who had just been appointed to a curatorship at the Cleveland Museum of Natural History, recruited the services of James Aronson, a K/Ar dating specialist at Case Western Reserve University in the same city. Taieb had already located a datable lava flow at Hadar, plus some thin tuffs, and in 1974 Aronson visited Hadar to collect datable samples. Aronson was able more precisely to fix the position of the lava flow in the Hadar stratigraphy, and following his return to Cleveland dated it at over 3 myr, confirming preliminary dates on a sample collected earlier. Nonetheless, because of suspected weathering of the lava samples (which would have resulted in the loss of accumulated argon and thus an underestimate of the true age), it remained possible that the lava was in fact somewhat older. At the top of the section, a capping date of 2.6 myr was obtained on a tuff; this resulted in an estimated age for Lucy of about 2.9 myr, while the isolated jaws and the knee joint were older. For a variety of reasons uncertainties about the precise dating at Hadar lingered until the early 1990s, when it was found that all the many hominid fossils known by then came from a rather short span of time, between about 3.2 and 3.4 myr. Lucy was the youngest among them. This made Lucy older, and the older specimens somewhat younger, than had generally been thought.

The 1975 field season saw Ethiopia in political turmoil. Haile Selassie had been overthrown in 1974, his powers assumed by a Marxist military dictatorship that took some time to take a recognizable form. Nonetheless, Johanson and his colleagues managed to get back to the Afar, and they hit the jackpot yet again. This time it was the "First Family," an unbelievable trove of some 200 early human fossils, all jumbled up next to one another in the sediments. As in the case of Lucy, nothing resembling this had ever been found before. Site 333, as the locality at which these fossils were found became designated, eventually yielded the fragmentary remains of thirteen individuals, male and female, adult and juvenile. The circumstances by which the remains of all these hominids came to be buried together in the sediments have never been definitively figured out, but one suggestion was that all may have been caught together in a flash flood. If this is the case, then it is likely that all belonged to the same social group. And although one group doesn't make much of a statistical sample, if most of its members were represented among the fossils, this would tell you something about social group size—and thirteen individuals of all ages is not out of line with expectation.

More importantly, though, if all belonged to the same social group, then all belonged to the same species. Paleontologists almost invariably have to rely on inference in determining whether different fossil individuals in fact belonged to the same species; but here, potentially, is a demonstration of this by a totally different means. Disappointingly, however, there is no unanimity on this matter of burial; some claim that the fossils accumulated sequentially over some period of time, and the debate seems set to continue, which is particularly a shame because whether or not the Hadar hominids represent a single species continues to be a particularly contentious subject in paleoanthropology.

Despite continuing instability in Ethiopia, the Hagar team returned for further fieldwork in late 1976. Aside from more hominid fossils, notably many new ones from the "First Family" site, these researches resulted in the discovery by the archaeologist Hélène Roche of simple basalt tools dated at about 2.5 myr. Who had made these remarkably ancient tools remained problematic: no hominid fossils were known from this point in time, and in any case associating early stone tools with their makers has been a perennially tricky issue in paleoanthropology. Sadly, though it proved impossible to follow up on this find. For, as the result of another military coup in Addis Ababa, the end of the 1976–77 field season marked the effective cessation of work at Hadar: work which wouldn't resume on any major scale for well over a decade.

Bodo and Laetoli

It's probably appropriate to note here that the work at Hadar was not the only paleontology being pursued in Ethiopia during the mid-1970s. In 1976 the face of a massively built adult hominid was discovered by a team led by Johanson's rival Jon Kalb in the Middle Awash region of the Afar Depression. This specimen was found lying on sediments belonging to the Upper Bodo Beds. These contain abundant vertebrate fossils and Acheulean tools and were dated by Kalb and his associates to the Middle Pleistocene, perhaps about 400 kyr ago (with a very wide margin of error). Subsequent work has fixed the age of the Bodo cranium to about 600 myr ago. In Africa, the closest comparison of this specimen is with the famous "Rhodesian Man" cranium from Kabwe, Zambia. Judiciously enough, the Kalb team found the Bodo face to be less "archaic" than Asian *Homo erectus* or Olduvai Hominid 9, but to be more so than the Omo Kibish crania that Richard Leakey's group had discovered a few years earlier. We'll come back later to what that means; meanwhile, suffice it to note that during a brief survey of the same area in 1981, a group led by the veteran African archaeologist J. Desmond Clark recovered a couple of hominid fragments from very much older sediments dated at about 4 myr ago. These fossils consisted of a partial frontal bone and part of the proximal end of a femur belonging to a habitual upright biped. The frontal fragment was said by Clark and his colleagues to resemble an immature specimen known from the Tanzanian site of Laetoli, whither the focus of this story now shifts.

Laetoli, to recap, is the place about 25 miles southwest of Olduvai Gorge that was first visited by Louis and Mary Leakey in 1935. At that time they recovered an isolated lower canine tooth that Leakey thought belonged to a monkey, but which eventually turned out to have come from the jaw of an early hominid. There are several square kilometers at Laetoli over which sediments of Pliocene age are exposed, but there is much more grassy vegetation around than there is in the gorge at Olduvai. This makes it much less satisfactory from the fossil collector's point of view, so the elder Leakey rapidly turned his attentions to Olduvai, where he remained even after the German explorer Ludwig Kohl-Larsen turned up a human upper jaw fragment at Laetoli (or Garusi as he called it, for the river valley in which it lies) some four years later.

In 1950, as we've seen, Kohl-Larsen's compatriot Hans Weinert made this fragment the type specimen of the new species *Meganthropus africanus*, considering it allied to a problematic jaw fragment from Java that had been named by Franz Weidenreich in 1945. But it was not until four decades had elapsed after her first visit that Mary Leakey was to return to Laetoli to undertake prospections of any magnitude. These field researches lasted from 1974 to 1981 and yielded some thirty early hominid fossils, ranging from isolated teeth and jaw fragments to two quite well-preserved adult lower jaws: one adult (Laetoli Hominid 4) and one juvenile (LH 2). Bits of a juvenile skeleton were also recovered. Another find was of a much later and reasonably complete human skull (LH 18, known as the Ngaloba skull after the deposits in which it was found); this is somewhat archaic in appearance and has an estimated brain volume of 1200 ml. K/Ar dating on tuffs revealed that the two jaws were between 3.6 and 3.8 myr old; the Ngaloba specimen is probably in the region of 150 kyr old.

The real jewel of Laetoli, however, was a number of footprint trails preserved in very fine volcanic ash, puffed out some 3.6 myr ago by the nearby volcano Sadiman. After this powder had settled in a thin layer on the landscape, a light rain fell, turning it to something like wet cement. Before it dried out and hardened, various birds and mammals wandered over it, leaving their prints behind. Among the mammals were some early hominids, and incredibly at one place (Site G, excavated in 1978 and 1979) the preserved footprints of a pair of such creatures who had walked side by side were preserved over a total distance of about eighty feet. After the prints had been made and dried, the volcano erupted once more, emitting more ash that covered and protected them until they were exposed by erosion for the Leakey group to find.

This was, of course, a quite remarkable and unprecedented discovery. Most fossils provide direct evidence of bony or dental anatomy only. Any inferences about how their possessors had behaved—walked around, for instance—are just that, inferences. But here at Laetoli early human behavior itself was fossilized! Of course, these were not the only footprints of ancient humans ever to be found: others are known, for instance, from several Ice Age caves in Europe. But almost all the other fossil human footprints known are those of members of our own species, *Homo sapiens*, dating back at most a few tens of thousands of years. The Laetoli prints, in contrast, reflect the origins of the human lineage; they are the only tracks so ancient that the creatures who made them might conceivably not have been fully bipedal—who might not have walked more or less as we do.

Of course, the world being the imperfect place it is, full agreement over the implications of the prints was long in coming—has not, indeed, been achieved yet, although nobody disputes that they are the traces left behind by upright bipeds. Similar disagreement surrounds the interpretation of the hominid fossils from Laetoli, although initially these crept quite discreetly into the literature. The jaws and teeth found at Laetoli were given for description to Tim White, a student of Milford Wolpoff's who had worked briefly at east Turkana before falling out with Richard Leakey, and who later spent the 1978 field season (when the majority of the prints were excavated) at Laetoli before falling out with Mary Leakey. In 1977, White produced a low-key and meticulous description in fine print of the Laetoli hominids discovered in 1974 and 1975 without making any comment whatever about their affinities. Descriptions of the later finds followed in 1980. I recall colleagues complaining at the time how unreadably boring these descriptions were, but—as he would shortly prove—this was hardly due to any shortage of imagination on White's part; he was simply hewing closely to a policy that the Leakeys were by then imposing on all their collaborators.

One Species or Two?

So what was this ancient biped of Laetoli, effectively the earliest hominid known? The first attempt to answer this had to await a collaboration between White and Don Johanson. Between them, these two researchers were responsible for the description of virtually all the hominid fossils known then from the period between about 4 and 3 myr ago, and it might have seemed natural that the two should have ended up collaborating on an analysis of these fossils despite the fact that they were of very different temperaments. In any event, in the summer of 1977 Johanson asked White to bring casts of the Laetoli fossils to Cleveland for comparison with those from Hadar. The obvious question was: Did the hominids from the two sites belong to the same species?

Disagreement between Johanson and White on this point was to be expected; after all, Johanson had already claimed in print that several species might be represented among the Hadar fossils, while White had trained under Milford Wolpoff, the guru of the single-species philosophy that rejected the idea that more than one hominid species could exist at any one point in time. And by Johanson's account disagreement there was, at least to start with. One problem was that there was an enormous range in size between the biggest and the smallest individuals represented among the Hadar fossils. And there were differences in morphology, too; for example, while the tiny Lucy had very diminutive front teeth (hence the rather V-shaped jaw), bigger jaws from Hadar had relatively larger front teeth. In one perspective, the size differences might simply have been the result of very substantial sexual dimorphism within a single species, the larger fossils representing males and the smaller ones females. In that case, the shape differences would very likely have been no more than passive consequences of size discrepancies. The influence of size on shape ("allometry") had, after all, been documented long since among living organisms of all kinds. Alternatively, both size and shape differences might have been accounted for by the presence of more than one species in the sample. White favored the single-species view, despite the huge disparity in size between the largest individuals and the smallest ones. To begin with, at least, Johanson preferred the two-species interpretation he had already espoused, with the larger specimens representing some primitive species of *Homo*, and Lucy and her like something else.

The first conclusion the pair agreed upon was that all the Hadar hominids were distinct both from apes and other known hominids. Then it became evident to them that in many features a gradation in size from large to small was present within the sample, so that the question of shape differences became paramount. In the end they satisfied themselves that the shape differences were adequately accounted for by allometry, plus the differences that always occur between different individuals of the same species. At Hadar and Laetoli, between about 3.7 and 3 myr ago they thus saw evidence of a single species of hominid that was unlike any other. This species was fully bipedal, and males were much bigger than females (somewhat as among gorillas today) though even males probably didn't stand a lot taller than four and a half feet. To judge from the pronounced muscle attachment scars on the bones, both sexes had been powerfully built. Their legs were shorter in proportion to the arms than ours are today, and their hands were like human ones in most details, though they were a bit longer and more curved. Their torsos tapered upwards. Their brains were small, in the chimpanzee range, and, again like those of apes, their faces were large and projecting. Their toothrows converged a little toward the front, forming an arcade that was neither parabolic, as in modern humans, nor parallel-sided, as among living apes. The incisors were large, though not extraordinarily so; and while the canines were conical, as in apes, they resembled those of humans in their reduced size. The molar teeth were large and relatively flat. These distinctive hominids predated the earliest stone tools known from Hadar and almost certainly were nor toolmakers.

Here, then, Johanson and White had evidence for a new species of hominid, one earlier than any other known. But a species of what genus? There were only two choices offer: *Australopithecus* and *Homo*, and nobody who didn't wish to be hooted out of the profession would have dreamed of creating a new genus. Based more than anything else on the age of their new creature, they decided that what they had here was a stem hominid, ancestral to all subsequent human species. And if this ancestor had given rise to *Australopithecus* as well as *Homo* species, they reasoned, it couldn't itself be *Homo*. The logic of this particular proposition is not entirely clear (for if a genus located at the fork of a V can be given the name of one of the two at the ends of the branches, it can equally well be given that of the other); but there's no doubt that given the reigning intellectual climate it was the more palatable choice. For to have called this creature a member of *Homo* would effectively have been to make our own genus equivalent to the entire expanding family Hominidae.

So the genus *Australopithecus* was selected. What was the new species to be named? Given that the fossils came from two widely separated sites, Johanson and White wanted to bind them together symbolically. This they achieved by making the Laetoli mandible LH 4 the type specimen of their new species and by calling that species *Australopithecus afarensis*, for the Afar region of Ethiopia that had yielded most of the specimens assigned to it. This, though legal, was not in fact very good procedure, for it was a good bet that someone would come along and claim that the Laetoli and Hadar materials in fact belong to different species—as has indeed happened. In the (not unlikely) event that such distinctiveness is conclusively demonstrated, the name *afarensis* will have to stay with the Tanzanian type specimen. The chosen name did, however, reflect the strength of Johanson's and White's conviction that only a single species existed at the two sites; and perhaps unexpectedly, most criticism of this idea, when it came, focused not so much on differences between the two sites as on whether more than one species might be recognized among the multitude of fossils known from Hadar.

A Stem Hominid?

The single-species idea conflicted, of course, with the views that Richard Leakey was propounding on the basis of his Koobi Fora fossils—especially given the very early date that he was still assigning to the KBS tuff. Although Leakey had never been very specific about his views on the pattern of early human evolution, his publications showed clearly that he believed, like his father, in the separation of the *Homo* and *Australopithecus* lineages from the very earliest times; to see them converging, as claimed by Johanson and White, was unpalatable to say the least. The first rumblings of trouble came in 1978, when Mary Leakey attended the meeting in Stockholm at which Johanson made the initial public announcement of *Australopithecus afarensis*. Mary had been intending to discuss the Laetoli hominids, and according to Johanson she was affronted to hear him talking about "her" specimens, even though they had been described in print and thus were in the public domain. Further, the implications of what he was saying about them were hardly congenial to her. By Johanson's account Mary had earlier agreed to join him, White, and Yves Coppens as coauthor on the publication describing the new species (with the proviso that it not suggest that any *Australopithecus* was ancestral to *Homo*; this was achieved by eliminating any discussion of the affinities of the new species). Now, however, she demanded that her name be taken off the article, something that at that stage could only be achieved by destroying the entire print run and publishing a new version. Personal relationships between the Leakeys and the Johanson/White axis became decidedly cooler.

While all this was going on, Johanson and White prepared an interpretive paper on *A. afarensis* that laid out their ideas on the place of this species in human evolution. The article was published at the beginning of 1979 in the influential journal *Science,* and it made headlines in the popular media as well as waves in the profession. In it the pair discussed various alternative possible arrangements among the hominid species that they recognized; and they plumped for a simple forking scheme whereby the stem species *A. afarensis* gave rise, some time after 3 myr ago, to two lineages. One of these led from *Homo* habilis through H. erectus to H. sapiens; the other led from *A. africanus* to *A. robustus,* which became extinct at about 1 myr ago. They did not recognize the Leakeys' species A. boisei as distinct from South African *A. robustus,* and they claimed that tendencies towards the robust condition were already detectable in *A. africanus* compared to the more primitive *A. afarensis.*

This (or, to be quite frank, virtually any other) interpretation was bound to cause an outcry, and not simply from the Leakeys. One might well, indeed, have expected the response to have been even more shrill than it actually was, but it was nonetheless hardly muted. Some critics were adamant that what Johanson and White had were actually East African representatives of the species *A. africanus,* already abundantly represented from South Africa though only questionably known in eastern Africa by a few isolated teeth from Omo. Ironically—because his own new species, *Homo habilis,* had suffered the identical criticism—South Africa's Phillip Tobias was foremost among such critics. Indeed, Tobias announced during the Stockholm conference at which *A. afarensis* made its debut that the Laetoli and Sterkfontein fossils merely represented subspecies (geographical variants) of *A. africanus.* He repeated this assertion in a long paper published in 1980 in which he claimed that it was the expanded species *A. africanus* that was the progenitor of all later hominids, including the robust australopiths on the one hand and *Homo* on the other.

At about the same time Todd Olson, then of New York's City College, reviewed the same question and concluded that the bulk of the Hadar specimens and those from Laetoli in fact belonged with the robust australopithecines—which he allocated to Broom's genus *Paranthropus.* Most specifically, he found *Paranthropus* characteristics in skull base fragments from Hadar. Accepting the priority of Kohl-Larsen's species name for the Laetoli jaws and teeth (and by extension, for the larger Hadar specimens), he allocated these East African fossils to the species *Paranthropus africanus*. On the other hand, he claimed that the smallest of the Hadar specimens, notably Lucy, were indeed different. These he placed in a primitive species of the genus *Homo*, and, like John Robinson, he extended this genus to embrace the gracile South African material. Thus in Olson's view the small Ethiopian fossils, plus those traditionally placed in *Australopithecus africanus*, all belonged to the species *Homo africanus*.

Another paleoanthropologist who now saw two (or maybe more) species among the Hadar fossils was Yves Coppens, whose students Brigitte Senut and Christine Tardieu had been studying the postcranial remains. Like Olson, these researchers arrived at the conclusion that two (or maybe more) species of hominid were represented at Hadar. However, Coppens saw Lucy, along with the bulk of the material, as a member of *Australopithecus afarensis*. It was various other arm and leg bones that they saw as belonging to a primitive species of *Homo*. And Richard Leakey, of course, continued to find evidence in the sample for both *Australopithecus* and *Homo*, although he offered no detailed reasons for this perception.

The argument continues; but the Johanson/White interpretation that only a single hominid species occurred at Laetoli and Hadar quite rapidly carried the day among most paleoanthropologists, at least as a working hypothesis. Indeed, *Australopithecus afarensis* entered the accepted pantheon of ancient human precursors a good bit more rapidly than had any fossil human species previously named. But fossils are not, of course, just static objects that merely sit gathering dust in museum drawers when we are not trying to find out from them to which other fossils they are most closely related. In the final analysis they are the only witnesses we have to a long and dynamic and eventful story: a story of creatures struggling to survive and to perpetuate themselves within an environment that tends—wherever on the Earth—to be both dangerous and unpredictably changeable. And how our ancestors coped with such vagaries constitutes a significant part of the evolutionary story of our lineage.

Bipeds and Climbers?

At the time when *Australopithecus afarensis* was described, common wisdom ascribed the adoption of bipedalism to the need to free the hands to make tools and to carry them and other objects around. But the discovery that this upright biped was already up on its hind feet a good million years before stone tools appeared in the archaeological record obviously meant that some rethinking was called for. The most elaborate of this rethinking was done by Owen Lovejoy, of Kent State University, to whom Johanson had entrusted the description of much of the hominid postcranial material from Hadar. Lovejoy's analysis of the Lucy skeleton and other fossils convinced him that here was not only an upright biped, but a creature that was very efficiently adapted to an upright striding gait. He found, for example, that Lucy's restored pelvis not only showed all the hallmarks of our own, but additionally had more widely flaring ilia (the "blades" of the pelvis). In combination with a longer neck to the femur, this attribute improved the mechanical advantage of the muscles that stabilize the hip in the upright position. And this was possible, Lovejoy reasoned, because the small-brained *A. afarensis* simply didn't need to make the compromises that are necessary in modern humans to allow the passage through the birth canal of a large-brained newborn. He thus concluded that in *A. afarensis* upright bipedalism was in fact more efficient than it is in ourselves.

This conclusion hasn't gone unchallenged. Their studies of the bones of the upper and lower limbs suggested to Senut and Tardieu that joint mobility was greater in *A. afarensis* than in modern humans, implying greater climbing capabilities. Bill Jungers of the State University of New York at Stony Brook pointed out that while Lucy's arms were proportionately not much longer than those of modern people, her legs were shorter, which would favor climbing. Russ Tuttle of the University of Chicago found that the length and curvature of the bones of the hands and feet suggested a strong grasping, hence climbing, capability. Henry McHenry noted high mobility in the wrist joint, which carries similar implications. Putting all this together, Jungers and his Stony Brook colleagues Randy Susman and Jack Stern concluded that whereas *A. afarensis* was undoubtedly bipedal while on the ground, it probably spent a good deal of time in the trees. They felt it likely that at night these early hominids sheltered from predators in trees, and probably also foraged there in the daytime, too.

How you look at all of this depends, of course, on which characteristics you think are most important in determining habitual behaviors. Nobody disputes that *A. afarensis* was descended at some remove from a largely tree-dwelling ancestor, although we have to bear in mind that modern great apes all spend more or less time on the ground. Obviously, terrestrial bipedalism was not acquired full-blown overnight in its full anatomical splendor, so we would expect newly bipedal hominids to show some evidence of their arboreal ancestry in their skeletal structure. And if we thus expect to find a mosaic of terrestrial and arboreal characteristics in the first habitual bipeds, which of those characteristics should we regard as most informative about behavior? Although the only plausible reason that a hominoid coming to the ground would adopt a bipedal gait there is because it was the most comfortable thing to do—because, in other words, the arboreal ancestor already habitually held its trunk upright when moving around in the trees—it is nonetheless close to certain that the newly acquired (in this case, terrestrial) features of *A. afarensis* reflect behaviors in which the species actually indulged—for why else would they have become established? So as far as the behavioral repertoire of the early terrestrial bipeds is concerned, the big question reposes on how much the ancestral tree-climbing capacity was actually used.

Australopithecus afarensis at Hadar lived in an environment that consisted of a mosaic of riverine gallery forests and more open savanna habitats, and it presumably moved through regions of both kinds (the arid grassland environment in which the Laetoli hominids left their tracks was almost certainly not typical of where they found the bulk of their sustenance). What's more, though robust, *A. afarensis* was small-bodied; and, being bipedal, it wasn't very fast. Presumably, then, this hominid was pretty vulnerable to open-country predators, and as a reasonably accomplished climber it would hardly have refrained from using trees for shelter, particularly at night. Further while tree-borne fruits would have been easily accessible to these creatures, as far as we know they did not make stone tools (although there is no reason to suppose that they might not have availed themselves of various soft materials, as chimpanzees do). A lack of hard tools would, however, have limited their access to many of the resources—roots, bulbs, tubers and so forth—that were potentially available on the savanna. In the deadly serious game of survival it's highly unlikely that *A. afarensis* would not have used every resource at its disposal, so on balance a behavior pattern that combined its climbing abilities with its newfound bipedal capacity seems probable. And since the anatomical structure typified by Lucy seems to have endured for several million years, this was clearly a successful behavioral strategy.

Why Bipedality?

The exact interpretation of the functional anatomy of Lucy and her kin is still disputed. It's claimed, for instance, that *A. afarensis* could not have fully extended its knee as we do, while the head (the weight-bearing portion) of the femur is much smaller than it is in ourselves, suggesting a less complete adaptation to upright posture. Nonetheless, the essentials of bipedal locomotion were undoubtedly there, and few would doubt now that bipedalism was the primordial hominid adaptation. This leads to the obvious question: Why? Owen Lovejoy thought he had the answer. In 1981 he published a paper arguing that, since the anatomically and behaviorally complex transition from ape-style quadrupedalism to upright posture could not have taken place in a single fell swoop, there must have been some countervailing advantage that increased the reproductive success of the neither-fish-nor-fowl early hominids. By themselves the females couldn't do much to increase their rate of reproduction since they were already hampered by offspring that took years to become independent. But they could achieve that result by co-opting males into the feeding of the family. Unencumbered males were better able to roam around the landscape and, if bipedal, would have had their hands free to carry food home. However, they could only benefit reproductively from such an arrangement if the offspring whose survival prospects they thereby increased were actually their own. This conveniently meshed with the females' obvious interest in having a permanent mate to depend upon. In this way Lovejoy ingeniously wove bipedalism, food carrying, and ranging around home bases into a scenario that also involved the development of pair bonding and fidelity among early hominids. In turn, through the system of permanent sexual signals that reinforced it, this bonding accounted for the marked but famously hard to explain secondary sexual differences (facial hair and prominent breasts, for instance) that distinguish human males and females.

Predictably, Lovejoy's ideas ran into a lot of criticism on a whole variety of grounds. But they had the virtue of opening up the question of the origins of human bipedalism to an intensive reexamination. There was much discussion, for instance, of the energetics of bipedal locomotion, both in the style of humans and in that of modern great apes, all of which have a propensity for carrying their trunks upright at least under certain circumstances. Peter Rodman and Henry McHenry of the University of California at Davis, for example, showed quite elegantly in 1980 that while human bipedality is indeed inefficient compared with the quadrupedalism of a committed terrestrial mammal such as a horse, it is actually relatively efficient compared to terrestrial quadrupedalism in the ape style (which necessarily represents a compromise with locomotion in the trees). If an ape found itself having to cover long distances on the ground (as might happen as the forests in which it lived were fragmented by encroaching grassland), bipedalism might indeed be the most efficient form of locomotion for it to adopt. According to Rodman and McHenry, there was no need to invoke a fancy behavioral advantage to explain the transition from hominoid-style quadrupedalism to bipedalism simply because it could have made good energetic sense all by itself: there was no unbridgeable energetic gulf to be crossed between hominoid quadrupedalism and hominid bipedalism.

This kind of argument fit well into a burgeoning scrutiny of the role of environmental change in the adoption of hominid bipedalism—especially after it was found that the origin of the human family probably coincided reasonably closely with a drying episode in Africa. During this drawn-out event forest cover on the continent shrank considerably and was replaced by grasslands over wide areas. The most interesting recent speculations have centered on the changed physiological demands that faced the protohominids as they began to emerge into this new environment while their ape cousins remained confined to the steadily diminishing forests. For example, the English physiologist Pete Wheeler has explained how problems of body temperature regulation together with a shortage of drinking water, must have challenged these human precursors—and how bipedalism must have helped to meet that challenge.

Perhaps the most critical physiological problem facing any savanna-living mammal is cooling the brain, an organ that is highly sensitive to any overheating. Most savanna mammals have special mechanisms devoted to this function but, as forest dwellers, most primates don't. The only means available to the first hominids for cooling the brain was thus to keep the whole body cool—and one way of doing this was to minimize the incoming heat load imposed by the tropical sun. This is precisely what an upright posture achieves, by reducing the area of the body exposed to the suns direct rays. What's more, bipedalism raises the body far off the ground, where it can be cooled by the wind. In this way heat is lost by convection as well as by the evaporation of sweat—especially if the skin is not insulated by the dense hairy coat that bipedal posture makes it advantagous to shed. It is also virtually certain that early savanna-dwelling hominids would have had to range fairly widely to find food, and Wheeler calculated that at slow speeds human bipedalism demands less energy than ape quadrupedalism. This means that less internal body heat is generated as a byproduct of energy production.

With less heat generated internally and less absorbed from the environment, and a larger proportion of the body's surface area sheltered from the sun's direct rays and thus available for radiative cooling, body temperature regulation in the tropic environment ceases to be a critical problem. Wheeler believes that the arboreal ancestors of the first human bipeds were almost certainly not committed quadrupeds; rather, they were semi-arboreal generalists which already had a propensity to hold the trunk upright. When the forests in which they had lived began to fragment and to be replaced by sun-scorched grasslands, they thus had a number of options open to them as they began to exploit the new environment; and the physiological advantages of upright posture may have been enough to tip the balance in favor of bipedal locomotion.

Later humans developed specialized means of cooling the brain, notably a "radiator" composed of tiny veins in the scalp and face. Dean Falk of Florida State University points out that this mechanism is lacking in living apes. What's more, to judge from features of the inside of the braincase that are associated with such cooling, it was also absent in the hominids from Hadar and in the robust australopithecines. Falk claims, though, that the pattern of cranial blood circulation differs in the one (juvenile) specimen from Laetoli that bears on this issue. In her view, this may place the Laetoli and Hadar fossils not simply in different species but in different lineages, the former lying on the way to gracile *Australopithecus* and *Homo*, and the latter giving rise to the robust australopithecines. This is not an interpretation that has attracted a lot of support, but it is the kind of finding that raises questions about how we interpret the fossil data at our disposal. And since the heyday of fossil hominid discoveries in Kenya and Ethiopia began in the early and middle 1970s, there have been twin revolutions in the ways in which paleoanthropologists—and paleontologists in general—view both the evolutionary process and the fossil record of evolutionary history. We'll look at those revolutions in the next chapter.

Faulty Genes, Coding for Faulty Enzymes Can Lead to Sickness

JAY PHELAN

sabella joins her friends in sipping wine during a dinner party. As the meal progresses, her companions become tipsy. Their conversations turn racy, their moods relaxed. They refill their glasses, reveling in a little buzz. Not so for Isabella. Before her first glass is empty, she experiences a "fast-flush" response: her face turns crimson, her heart begins to race, and her head starts to pound. Worse still, she soon feels the need to vomit.

How can people respond so differently to alcohol? It comes down to a difference in a single base pair in their DNA, a single difference that can influence dramatically a person's behavior, digestion, respiration, and general ability to function. The base-pair change leads to the production of a non-functional enzyme, and the lack of a functional version of this enzyme leads to physical illness. Let's look at the details.

When we consume alcohol, our bodies start a two-step process to convert the alcohol molecules from their intoxicating form into innocuous molecules. Each of the two steps is made possible by a specific enzyme, whose assembly instructions are coded in the DNA of most people.

Fast-flushers like Isabella complete the first step of breaking down alcohol, but cannot complete the breakdown because they carry defective genetic instructions for making aldehyde dehydrogenase, the enzyme that makes possible the second step of the process. A poisonous substance subsequently accumulates, and the symptoms of the "fast-flush" reaction are due to this substance's toxic effects in the body.

Why do many Asians have unpleasant experiences associated with alcohol consumption? Approximately half of the people living in Asia carry a non-functional form of the

Jay Phelan, Ed., "Faulty Genes, Coding for Faulty Enzymes can Lead to Sickness," from *What Is Life?: A Guide to Biology*, pp. 177–178. Copyright © 2010 by W.H. Freeman and Company. Permission to reprint granted by the publisher.

gene for aldehyde dehydrogenase, a mutation that may confer a greater benefit than harm. In a study of 1,300 alcoholics in Japan, not a single one was a fast-flusher, even though half of all Japanese people are fast-flushers. The minor change in the genetic code that makes alcohol consumption an unpleasant experience may be responsible for the lower incidence of alcoholism among Japanese and other Asian people.

In many other cases—perhaps in the majority of genetic diseases—the link between a particular defective DNA sequence and physical illness is equally direct. Recall from Chapter 3 the case of Tay-Sachs disease. In Tay-Sachs disease, an individual inherits genes with a mutation that causes an inability to produce a critical lipid-digesting enzyme in their lysosomes, the cellular garbage disposals. Because these organelles cannot digest certain lipids, the lipids accumulate, undigested. The lysosomes swell until they eventually choke the cell to death. This occurs in numerous cells in the first few years of life, and ultimately leads to the child's death.

Although the details differ from case to case, the overall picture is the same for many, if not most, inherited diseases. The pathway from mutation to illness includes just four short steps.

1. A mutated gene codes for a non-functioning protein, commonly an enzyme.
2. The non-functioning enzyme can't catalyze the reaction as it normally would, bringing the reaction to a halt.
3. The molecule with which the enzyme would have reacted accumulates, just as half-made products would pile up on a blocked assembly line.
4. The accumulating chemical causes sickness and/or death.

The fact that most genetic diseases involve illnesses brought about by faulty enzymes suggests some strategies for treatment. These include administering medications that contain the normal-functioning version of the enzyme. For instance, lactose-intolerant individuals can consume the enzyme lactase, which for a short while gives them the ability to digest lactose. Alternatively, lactose-intolerant individuals can reduce their consumption of lactose-containing foods to keep the chemical from accumulating, thus reducing the problems that come from its overabundance.

The Sex of Offspring Is Determined in a Variety of Ways in Non-human Species

JAY PHELAN

For something as fundamental to a species as sex determination, you might imagine that one method evolved and all species use it. The world is more diverse than that. In most plants there aren't even distinct males and females. In corn, for example, every individual produces both male and female gametes. All earthworms and garden snails are also capable of producing both male and female gametes. Such organisms are called **hermaphrodites** (from the names of the Greek god Hermes and goddess Aphrodite) because both male and female gametes are produced by an individual. But even among the species with separate males and females there are several different methods of sex determination. The human method, in which having both an X and a Y chromosome makes you male and having two X chromosomes makes you female, is common among eukaryotes and is seen in all mammals. But it is only one of at least four different methods used by organisms for determining sex. We'll examine the three others, used by different groups, here.

BIRDS

In birds, the mother determines the sex in a way that is similar to the way fathers determine sex in humans. Females have one copy of two different sex chromosomes, called the Z and the W chromosomes. Males, on the other hand, have only one type, carrying two copies of the Z chromosome. Consequently, the sex of bird offspring is determined by the mother rather than the father. This method is also found in some fish and butterfly species.

ANTS, BEES, AND WASPS

In these insects, sex is determined by the number of chromosome sets an individual possesses. Males are haploid, having only a single set of chromosomes, and females are diploid, carrying two full sets of chromosomes. In this unusual method, females produce haploid eggs by meiosis. They then mate with males and store the sperm in a sac. As each egg is produced, the female can allow it to be fertilized by some of the sperm she has stored, in which case the offspring will be diploid and female. Alternatively, she can lay the unfertilized egg, which can develop into a haploid, male individual. Just think, in these species, males don't have a father, yet they do have a grandfather.

TURTLES

In some species, sex determination is controlled by the environment rather than by the number or types of chromosomes an organism has. In most turtles, for example, offspring sex is determined by the temperature at which the eggs are kept. Eggs that are kept relatively hot during incubation become females, while the eggs incubated at slightly cooler temperatures become males. The sex of some lizards and crocodiles is also determined by the temperature at which the eggs are incubated.

TAKE–HOME MESSAGE

A variety of methods are used for sex determination across the world of plant and animal species. These include the presence or absence of sex chromosomes, the number of chromosome sets, and environmental factors such as incubation temperature.

"Before Darwin, Most People Believed That All Species Had Been Created Separately and Were Unchanging" by Jay Phelan from What is Life? A Guide to Biology, © 2010 W. H. Freeman & Co..

"Darwin and After" by Ian Tattersall from The Fossil Trail: How We Know What We Think We Know About Human Evolution, © 2009 Oxford University Press.

"Human Welfare Program" by Dr. I.J.S Bansal from Biological Physical Anthology, © 2011 .

"Walking Through Time" by Robert Boyd and Joan B. Silk from How Humans Evolved, Third Edition, © 2002 W. W. Norton & Co., Inc..

"The Evolution of Menstruation" by Robert Boyd and Joan B. Silk from How Humans Evolved, Third Edition, © 2002 W. W. Norton & Co., Inc..

"Heredity: Living Code in a Coil" by Sarah H. Riedman from Biological Physical Anthology, © 2011 .

"Death and the Sexes" by John F. Kalinich & Max Fogiel from Genetics: Unlocking the Mysteries of Life, © 2000 Research & Education Association .

"Organisms by Design" by John F. Kalinich & Max Fogiel from Genetics: Unlocking the Mysteries of Life, © 2000 Research & Education Association .

"Got Milk?" by Robert Boyd and Joan B. Silk from A Natural History of Parenting: From Emperor Penguins to Reluctant Ewes, A Naturalist Looks at Parenting in the Animal World and Ours, © 1997 Harmony Books/ Crown Publishing Group.

"The Human Brain" by Sarah R. Riedman from Biological Physical Anthology, © 2011 .

"The Evolution of Skin Color" by Sarah R. Riedman from Human Biological Variation, by James H. Mielke, Lyle W. Konigsberg & John H. Relethford, © 2005 Oxford University Press.

"What is Sex For?" by Jeremy Cherfas & John Gribbin from The Redundant Male: Is Sex Irrelevant in the Modern World?, © 1984 Random House, Inc..

"Blood Pressure" by L.L. Langley from Homeostasis: Origins of the Concept, © 1973 Dowden & Culver, Inc..

"Hadar, Lucy, and Laetoli" by Ian Tattersall from The Fossil Trail: How We Know What We Think We Know About Human Evolution, © 2009 Oxford University Press.

Published by Montezuma Publishing.

Please direct comments regarding this product to:

> Montezuma Publishing
> Aztec Shops Ltd.
> San Diego State University
> San Diego, California 92182-1701
> 619-594-7552

or email: *orders@montezumapublishing.com*

website: www.montezumapublishing.com

Production Credits
> Production mastering by: Janel Bruan
> Quality control by: Stephanie Bryce
> Rights to reproduce copyrighted material procured by: Sara St. Jean

If the quality of some sections in this reader appear poor, it is due to the nature of the originals.
We have made every effort to ensure the best possible reproduction.

ISBN-10:   0-7442-0773-8
ISBN-13: 978-0-7442-0773-6

This anthology contains copyrighted material requiring payment of royalties to the publisher of $19.19.

CPSIA information can be obtained
at www.ICGtesting.com
Printed in the USA
FSOW02n0815190516
20536FS